Feed Your Health

The nutritionist's guide to easy, delicious home cooking

Alli Godbold

Feed Your Health
The nutritionist's guide to easy, delicious home cooking

©Alli Godbold

ISBN: 978-1906316-69-3

Published in 2010 by HotHive Books, Evesham, UK.
www.thehothive.com

Printed in the UK by Cambrian Printers

For mum, with all my love *x*

Contents

Introduction

So finally I am writing a book – something I have been promising to do for years but have always put off – chiefly because I am madly busy being a mum to three young children as well as being a nutritional therapist and hosting weekly cookery workshops from my kitchen.

This is hopefully going to be the first of a number of books that combines straight forward, healthy and, above all, delicious recipes with top tips for optimal health.

I am passionate about healthy food, not 70s style lentil loaf type of food – I am a foodie, I adore eating so my food has to taste great as well as being good for your health. I want you to flick through these recipes and be inspired and excited about cooking, my hope is that you will be motivated to get stuck in and start cooking right away.

I am a nutritional therapist. In simple terms, that means I see clients, explore their health problems and work out a diet plan to help them improve their well being. I have been doing this since qualifying in 1996 and over the years have come to realise just how scared of cooking so many people are. If not exactly scared they are apprehensive,

they think it takes too much time, organisation and effort. Many of my clients are busy men and women who work stupidly long hours, once home they want to be eating within 30 minutes with minimum fuss. This usually translates into eating a ready meal bought hastily from the supermarket on the way home. How can it be, with so much access to cookery on TV, on the magazine shelves and book shelves, that people are not cooking for themselves? I promise you, it really does not have to be time consuming, you don't need any tricky skills, it should be easy, satisfying and no big deal. Being able to cook allows you to really look after your health.

Aghast at just how many ready meals are being eaten, I started holding cookery workshops to show my clients how easy cooking can be – I wanted to show them how, by using fresh, natural and

unprocessed ingredients, they too could turn out delicious, healthy and simple dishes in no time at all. Making your own food is really rewarding, you know what has gone into it, you feel a sense of achievement, it is good for your health – what more could you ask for?!

To cut a long story short, I now hold cookery workshops nearly every week, I have some very loyal regulars, which means I have to keep creating new recipes to keep them coming back for more. Clients have been asking me for ages if I am going to publish a book of my favourite recipes, so here it is. I hope you like it, that you will use it and that some of these recipes will become firm favourites that you can pass on to others.

Feed your health essentials

Feeding your health is not difficult, you just need to get organised. That means shopping and stocking your fridge and kitchen cupboards with some basics – once you have these it's all so much easier.

Kitchen cupboard

Spices: turmeric, cumin seeds, coriander seeds, mustard seeds, garam masala, paprika, mixed spice, sumac, ground cinnamon, ground nutmeg, cinnamon sticks, cardamom pods, mace

Dried oregano

Dried kaffir lime leaves, dried curry leaves, bay leaves

Sushi nori sheets, Vietnamese rice wrappers

Desiccated coconut, ground almonds, oats, Pertwood Organics muesli

Brown rice flour, Doves Farm brown bread gluten free flour

Vanilla extract

Xanthan gum

Baking powder

Xylitol, agave nectar

Japanese brown rice vinegar, mirin, tamari soy sauce, Thai fish sauce

Marigold bouillon powder – reduced salt

Coconut milk

Extra virgin olive oil

Black peppercorns, sea salt

Tins of tomatoes, chickpeas, butter beans, kidney beans

Tomato purée

Buckwheat noodles, Thai rice noodles

Puy and red lentils

Red wine vinegar

Onions, garlic, lemons and limes

Fridge

Harissa sauce

Cold pressed, organic, extra virgin coconut butter

Hemp seed oil

Sesame seeds, sunflower seeds, pumpkin seeds

Cashews, pistachios, walnuts, flaked almonds

Fresh ginger

Lemon grass

Chillies

Natural yoghurt

Freezer

Berries

Broad beans

Sweetcorn

King prawns

With these ingredients you can rustle up no end of dishes. You will just need to buy the fresh veggies and fish or chicken to make amazing meals.

How to feed your health

A large part of my work is seeing clients for one-to-one consultations – and the issues that come up time and time again are lack of energy and weight gain.

I think that the most important rule for both increasing energy and for weight loss is to cut right back on sugar and refined carbohydrates (foods made with white flour, white pasta, white rice), that's why you will only see occasional use of brown sugar in the recipes. Instead I use xylitol, which is a natural sugar alternative, and agave nectar, another natural sweetener. Both are available from larger supermarkets or health food shops.

Sugar and refined carbs will only boost energy levels temporarily as they cause your body to produce a surge of the hormone insulin, which causes your blood sugar levels to come crashing down. This results in low energy. Insulin is a storage hormone so it also stops your body from burning fat for fuel, hindering weight loss.

I use quinoa, barley couscous, brown rice, buckwheat noodles, wholewheat flour, gluten free brown bread flour and brown rice flour instead of the usual refined, white options. Most of these are now available in large supermarkets but you may need to pay a visit to your local health food store for more of a choice.

The vast majority of my recipes can happily be eaten if you are trying to lose weight and where appropriate I have given some extra weight loss cooking

tips. For example, I will often suggest steam frying as this drastically reduces the amount of oil used in a recipe when sautéing onions and garlic, etc.

To steam fry you use just a teaspoon of olive oil and then add a little water – the oil coats the food so you still get the sautéd flavour, but the water means the food cooks in the steam reducing the need for extra oil. This method takes longer but significantly cuts down on fat.

Portion control is also critical for weight management as even healthy food can lead to weight gain if you eat enough of it! I always advise my clients to have no more than a fist-sized serving of heavy carbs – rice, bread, potatoes, etc – and an equal amount of protein at each meal. The best quality proteins are those contained in meat, poultry, fish and eggs, however red meats tend to contain rather too much saturated fat, so although it is fine to eat red meat in moderation, this book focuses on ways to include fish and chicken.

Another issue that many of my clients face is poor digestive health. Bloating, wind and constipation are so common they are almost considered normal by a lot of people and yet are often fairly simple to remedy. A lifetime of poor nutrition – too much red meat, sugar and refined carbs, not enough wholegrains, pulses, nuts and seeds, fruit and veg – can really mess up your digestive system and upset the balance of bacteria in your gut. Poor gut health results in

food intolerances, bloating, wind and constipation.

If you suffer from poor digestion it is definitely worth cutting down on wheat as this contains gluten. Gluten in the diet will often exacerbate digestive problems – it is a protein predominantly found in wheat but also in barley, rye and oats – for this reason many of the recipes are either gluten free or contain tips on how to make them gluten free.

The other food group you should pay attention to if you have digestive problems is dairy. Cut down on dairy products for a few weeks and monitor whether you experience any improvement in your symptoms. Many of us eat dairy throughout the day without even realising it – milk on our cereal, in lattes and cappuccinos, cheese at lunchtime, creamy sauces on our pasta... What we need is a wide variety of foods in the diet: too much of any one food increases our chances of developing an intolerance to it.

Many of my recipes are gluten and dairy free, which should make avoiding them much easier for you. Use the key below to identify which recipes will best suit your health needs.

DF dairy free	
GF gluten free	
WL suitable for those watching their weight	

All recipes serve four unless stated otherwise.

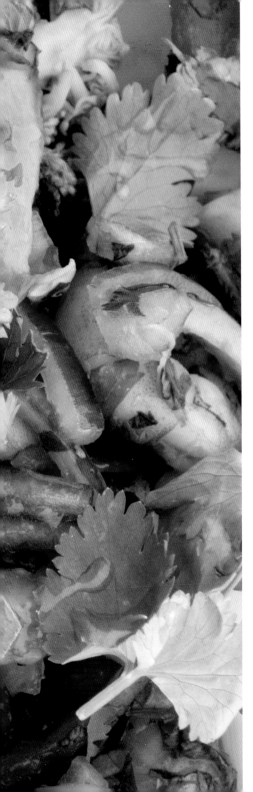

Salads

Avocado and tomato salad

I have been making this salad for years since I saw Antony Worrall Thompson making it on a TV show. It is so easy but tastes amazing, one of the nicest ways to eat avocados and perfect with the Easy Lemon Chicken recipe (see page 88).

Avocados contain oleic acid, a monounsaturated fat that may help to lower cholesterol. Avocados are also a good source of potassium, a mineral that helps regulate blood pressure. Adequate intake of potassium can help to guard against circulatory diseases, such as high blood pressure, heart disease or stroke. They are also a very concentrated dietary source of the carotenoid lutein – essential for eye health – and contain significant quantities of tocopherols (vitamin E).

DF GF WL

Cube the flesh of the avocados. Combine all the ingredients in a large bowl.

Easy!

ingredients

2 ripe Hass avocados

1 red onion, diced finely

1 large bunch coriander, washed, dried and chopped

1 punnet of sweet cherry tomatoes, halved

juice of 1 lime

sea salt and freshly ground black pepper

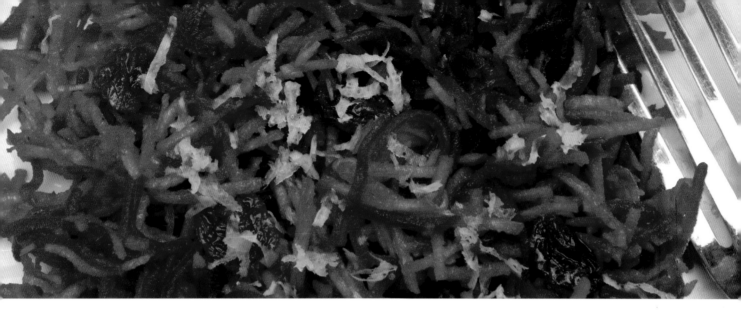

Beetroot salad

This is my good friend and chef, Al Wichart's, recipe for beetroot salad. He serves it on our in:spa retreats and it always goes down a treat with the guests. This salad goes well with the Turkey Meatballs (see page 90) and a green salad.

I like to use olive oil combined with a little hemp oil in this salad. Hemp oil is a good source of both omega 3 and 6 fats, and therefore good for both the immune and cardiovascular system. I buy 'Good Oil' hemp oil from the supermarket or health food shop.

Beetroot is a great source of folic acid and therefore important in pregnancy and for protecting the cardiovascular system. Traditionally beetroot is used for its cleansing and detoxifying properties.

DF **GF** **WL**

Combine the grated beetroot and carrot with the desiccated coconut, lemon zest and sultanas. Make a dressing by combining the oils with the lemon juice and season with black pepper. Combine the dressing with the salad.

ingredients

3 cooked beetroots, grated

5 carrots, grated

20g desiccated coconut

juice and zest of 1 lemon

20g sultanas

olive oil/hemp oil

freshly ground black pepper

Potato and sweet onion salad

This recipe is so delicious you must be strong with your portion control. The method of preparing the onions is great as it makes them more digestible. Fabulous for picnics and BBQs.

DF **GF** **WL** fine as long as you can stick to just a fist-sized amount!

Put the sliced onion in a small bowl and cover with cold water and salt. Leave to soak.

Meanwhile, boil the potatoes in salted water until tender, drain well.

Rinse the onion and drain, patting it dry on kitchen roll. Add to the potato with the remaining ingredients, season and mix well. Serve warm or at room temperature.

ingredients

1 red onion, very thinly sliced

a little salt

1 kg new potatoes, halved

2 tbs capers, drained and chopped

1 handful parsley, chopped

juice of 1 lemon

100g pitted black olives, roughly chopped

4 tbs olive oil

2 eggs, hard-boiled and mashed

sea salt and freshly ground black pepper

Red onion salad

I love this simple little salad, it goes so well with tzatsiki and focaccia or strips of wholemeal pitta bread. Soaking the onions really does stop them repeating on you for the rest of the day and so is well worth the effort.

One reason to choose red onions over white is that they contain more quercetin. Quercetin is an important antioxidant (helps prevent degenerative disease), it has anti-inflammatory properties and acts as an antihistamine and is therefore good to include if you suffer from allergies.

DF GF WL

Rinse the onions and put them into a bowl, cover with cold water, sprinkle with salt and leave for 30 minutes.

Rinse and drain the soaked onions in a sieve. Mix with the lemon juice and chilli and a splash of olive oil. Season with salt and pepper.

ingredients

2 red onions, finely chopped

2 tsp salt

juice of 1½ lemons

1 small red chilli,
seeded and finely chopped

olive oil

sea salt and freshly ground black pepper

Chickpea and feta salad

This is a fabulous salad and a good way to use chickpeas, I have made it time and time again at my workshops. There is something so comforting about the combination of creamy chickpeas and feta, there are never any leftovers!

Chickpeas and feta both supply protein so this is a satisfying salad on its own for lunch.

GF

WL go easy on the feta, perhaps halving the amount. Steam fry the onion, garlic and chilli in a teaspoon of olive oil with a little water

Rinse the chickpeas and put them in a bowl.

Heat 2 tbs of olive oil and fry the red onion gently until it is lightly golden. Add the garlic and chilli and cook for a few more seconds. Leave to cool.

Add the feta, spring onion, coriander, parsley and lemon juice to the chickpeas and season with black pepper and a little sea salt. Add the cooled garlic, chilli and onion and mix.

ingredients

400g tinned chickpeas

2 tbs olive oil

1 large red onion, finely chopped

5 garlic cloves, finely chopped

1 red chilli, deseeded and finely chopped

250g feta cheese, crumbled

4 spring onions, chopped

large handful coriander, chopped

large handful flat leaf parsley, chopped

juice of 1 lemon

sea salt and freshly ground black pepper

Pomegranate, chickpea and mint salad

This salad is an all time favourite of mine, the first time I had it was at a cookery demonstration given by Nanette Newman and Alison Price.
I often give it to friends for lunch and they always ask me for the recipe.
(See next recipe for the best way to get the seeds from the pomegranates.)

Pomegranates provide plenty of vitamin C, and are a good source of vitamin B5 (pantothenic acid) – both these nutrients are important for the adrenal glands, which pump out the stress hormones.

DF | **GF** | **WL**

Simply mix all the ingredients together and season well.

ingredients

4 spring onions, finely sliced

I garlic clove, finely chopped

I small handful of mint leaves, roughly shredded

I ½ tbs olive oil

400g tinned chickpeas, rinsed and drained

grated zest and juice of I lemon

seeds of 2 pomegranates

sea salt and freshly ground black pepper

Fennel, feta and pomegranate salad

This simple salad is another classic, it takes no time at all to prepare and tastes amazing. Anyone who hesitates about eating fennel will be a convert to the liquorice flavoured bulb, combined with these other ingredients, it is a taste sensation!

I find the best way to remove the seeds from the pomegranate is to cut the fruit into quarters and then pop the seeds out with my fingers, discarding any of the white pith or discoloured seeds. Make sure you wear an apron as the juice stains, and always assist a child with a pomegranate – the last time I let my son loose with one we had to have the kitchen repainted!

Sumac is a spice used in a lot of Middle Eastern cookery, it is derived from a small bitter berry and has a really distinctive sharp taste, you can find it in good delis and in the spice section of larger supermarkets.

Fennel contains the phytonutrient compound anethole. In animal studies, anethole has repeatedly been shown to reduce inflammation and to help prevent the occurrence of cancer.

GF | WL

Release the pomegranate seeds into a bowl.

Slice the fennel lengthwise into thin strips. In a bowl, mix the olive oil, sumac, lemon juice, herbs and a little salt and black pepper.

Add the fennel strips and toss in the dressing. Add the pomegranate seeds and feta.

Garnish with some more sumac and serve.

ingredients

seeds of 1 pomegranate

2 fennel heads, sliced lengthways

1 ½ tbs olive oil

2 tsp sumac, plus a little extra to garnish

juice of 1 lemon

4 tbs tarragon leaves

2 tbs flat leaf parsley, roughly chopped

salt and freshly ground black pepper

70g feta cheese, crumbled or bought in cubes

Prawn and mango salad

salads

This recipe is the invention of my friend and chef, Celia Brooks Brown. We were working together on ultimate recipes for healthy hair and this salad is chock-a-block with hair nourishing nutrients.

Blackstrap molasses is packed with iron, very important in protecting against hair loss.

Red peppers and broccoli are full of vitamin C, which is important for the absorption of iron.

Prawns are a good source of protein, very important for hair growth, and they are also a good source of zinc, which is needed for protein building.

If you prefer, you could use poached chicken in place of prawns (see Spicy chicken satay recipe on page 22 for poaching method).

DF **GF** **WL**

Whisk all the dressing ingredients together.

Combine the remaining ingredients in a bowl, toss together with the dressing and serve.

ingredients

for the dressing

1 garlic clove, peeled and finely chopped

1 fresh red chilli, finely chopped

2 tbs Thai fish sauce

2 tbs fresh lime juice

2 tbs molasses

for the salad

20 cooked tiger prawns

8-12 small broccoli florets, steamed and cooled

1 medium mango, peeled and cut into strips

1 red pepper, cut into thin strips

1 small red onion, peeled and finely sliced

1 large handful fresh mint, leaves stripped

1 large handful fresh coriander, chopped

Hot and sour Som Tum salad

I love this salad and could eat it every day, it tastes so clean and fresh. It works well as a starter or alongside some lightly steamed fish or poached chicken (see Spicy chicken satay recipe on page 22 for the best way to poach chicken).

Traditionally this salad would contain green papaya but it's quite hard to find and I think the turnip works brilliantly. The turnips are simple to grate if you have a magi mix, and in fact some of my guests have mistaken them for rice noodles.

Turnips are a great source of vitamins and minerals: calcium, potassium, magnesium and vitamin C, and eaten raw like this you are maximising their nutrient content.

DF | **GF** | **WL**

Make the dressing by pounding the garlic, chillies and salt to a paste in a heavy mortar, then whisk in the remaining ingredients.

Combine the grated turnip, sliced beans, pepper, tomato and onions with half of the cashews. Stir through the dressing and sprinkle on the remaining nuts.

ingredients

for the dressing

2 garlic cloves

1 red chilli, stem and seeds removed

½ tsp sea salt

4 tbs soy sauce

4 tbs lime juice

4 tbs xylitol (natural sugar alternative)

for the salad

300g baby turnip, grated

100g green beans, sliced

1 red pepper, deseeded and thinly sliced

1 tomato, cut into strips

4 spring onions, sliced

2 handfuls mint leaves

50g cashews, broken into pieces

Spicy chicken satay and noodle salad

I love serving this salad when I have friends over for lunch, it is really filling and perfect as a main course. It takes a little time but it's well worth it and if you reserve the stock you can use it to make a Tom Yum soup with prawns (see page 38) for your evening meal.

Peanuts contain healthy monosaturated fats which keep you feeling satisfied for longer and at the same time are cardio-protective.

DF	GF

WL don't be scared of the peanut butter – peanuts eaten in small quantities are not as risky as you think

Cut the chicken breasts into 3 or 4 pieces (to speed up the cooking time) and then poach in the stock for about 8 minutes (I like to use 1 litre of stock to which I add some lemon grass sticks, grated ginger and 2 tbs fish sauce). Cut a piece of chicken in half to check it is cooked all the way through. Once cooked, remove the chicken and allow it to cool.

Place the peanut butter, tamari soy sauce, lime juice, xylitol, sesame oil, chilli and garlic into food processor with the cold water. Purée and pour into a bowl.

Shred the chicken and combine with the peanut sauce.

In a large mixing bowl, place the pepper, cucumber, carrot and spring onions and add the coriander (reserving a few leaves for a garnish).

Prepare the noodles by placing them in a saucepan of boiling water, then take off the heat and leave for 5 minutes (or as directed on the packet), drain and run under cold water. Add the noodles to the vegetables.

Make the dressing by mixing the lime juice with the sesame oil and then adding the fish sauce. Pour over the noodle salad.

Divide the noodle salad between plates (six small plates for a starter portion, four plates for a main course), top with chicken satay and garnish with coriander leaves.

ingredients

for the spicy chicken

2 chicken breasts

1 litre vegetable stock
(made with reduced salt Marigold bouillon)

70g chunky sugar-free peanut butter

20ml tamari soy sauce

1 tbs lime juice

1 tsp xylitol (natural sugar alternative)

1 tbs toasted sesame oil

1 red chilli, finely chopped

1 clove garlic, finely chopped

3 tbs cold water

for the noodle salad

1 red pepper, quartered,
seeded and sliced thinly

¼ cucumber, finely sliced

1 large carrot, finely sliced

2 spring onions, finely sliced

1 large handful coriander leaves

125g rice noodles

2 tbs lime juice

2 tbs toasted sesame oil

1 tsp fish sauce

Coconut chicken salad

I made this salad for my friend Sybil's hen night and all the girls loved it. If you are feeling clever you could hang on to the poaching liquid and easily turn it into Thai coconut soup (see page 40).

This is a good way of getting cabbage into your diet; we don't eat enough cabbage and yet it definitely qualifies as a superfood.

New research is revealing that phytonutrients in cruciferous vegetables, such as cabbage, actually signal our genes to increase production of enzymes involved in detoxification, the cleansing process through which our bodies eliminate harmful compounds.

Recent studies show that those eating the most cruciferous vegetables have a much lower risk of prostate, colorectal and lung cancer – even when compared to those who regularly eat other vegetables.

Pour the coconut milk into a large saucepan, add the lime juice and lime leaves, chilli and chicken. Bring to the boil over a medium heat and simmer for about 8 minutes until the chicken is tender. Remove the chicken from the poaching liquid and set aside.

Make the dressing by pounding the chilli and garlic in a pestle and mortar, add the xylitol, lime juice, rice vinegar and fish sauce and stir.

Put the carrots and cabbage in a large bowl, along with the mint and coriander leaves and the spring onions. Coarsely shred the chicken into the salad using your fingers.

When ready to serve add the dressing and toss well to combine.

ingredients

for the chicken

400ml tin low fat coconut milk

5 tbs lime juice

2 large kaffir lime leaves, torn

1 fresh red chilli, finely sliced

2 organic chicken breasts, sliced into thirds

for the dressing

½ red chilli, finely chopped

1 clove garlic, finely chopped

1 dsp xylitol (natural sugar alternative)

3 tbs lime juice

1 tbs rice vinegar

1 tbs fish sauce

for the salad

1 bunch baby carrots, trimmed, scrubbed and chopped lengthways

¼ white cabbage, shredded

1 handful mint leaves

1 handful coriander leaves

3 spring onions, thinly sliced

salads

Barley cous cous

We all tend to eat way too much wheat so here is a fantastic alternative. Look for Beluza barley cous cous in the deli section of your supermarket.

This cous cous recipe couldn't be easier as it requires no cooking – simply cover the barley cous cous with orange juice, leave for 15 minutes and hey presto the cous cous 'cooks' in the acid from the juice.

Barley is an excellent source of fibre and nutrients including selenium and vitamin B3. Selenium is a major antioxidant and therefore cancer protective. B3 helps to keep blood sugar levels stable.

Put the cous cous in a bowl and cover with the orange juice.

While the cous cous is 'cooking' prepare the dressing:

Pound the garlic to a paste in a pestle and mortar with a little salt, add the lemon juice and cinnamon and another pinch of salt, stir in the olive oil. Season with a little pepper.

Fluff up the cous cous with a fork and combine with the salad ingredients and the dressing, mix well.

ingredients

for the cous cous

100g Beluza barley cous cous

freshly squeezed orange juice

for the dressing

1 clove garlic

sea salt and freshly ground black pepper

juice of 1 lemon

¼ tsp ground cinnamon

3 tbs extra virgin olive oil

for the salad

400g sweetest tomatoes, diced

4 spring onions, trimmed and chopped

3 small bunches of flat leaf parsley, roughly chopped (approximately 80g)

1 small bunch fresh mint leaves, roughly chopped

2 large handfuls of coriander leaves, roughly chopped

Quinoa and broad bean tabbouli

Quinoa is a grain which many of my clients have read about, bought and then kept unopened in their cupboards not having a clue what to do with it! I love to use it in a tabbouli type salad as I think quinoa works best with lots of dressing and salad veggies. Be careful not to overcook it – it can soon turn into a porridgy slop if you take your eye off it.

This is another Celia Brooks Brown 'healthy hair' recipe, packed with nutrients needed to keep your hair in tip top condition.

Quinoa is a great source of vegetarian protein, essential for hair growth.

Broad beans contain vitamin B5 – important for scalp health.

Apricots are a good source of iron – important for preventing hair loss.

DF	GF	WL

Heat a lidded saucepan over a moderate flame. Add the quinoa to the dry pan and shake until the grain is lightly toasted and popping. Add the stock, stir and reduce the heat to a simmer. Cover and cook for 10 minutes, then add the broad beans and apricots. Cook for a further 3-5 minutes, or just until the stock is absorbed but the grains are still separate. Spread the quinoa out on a large plate and allow it to cool.

Mix together the lemon zest and juice, olive oil and salt and pepper. When the quinoa is cool, combine in a bowl with the dressing, the chopped onion, herbs and tomato.

ingredients

200 ml quinoa, measured by volume in a measuring jug

400 ml vegetable stock (made with reduced salt Marigold bouillon)

200g frozen or fresh baby broad beans

8 dried apricots, chopped coarsely

grated zest of 1 large unwaxed lemon

juice of 1½ lemons

3 tbs extra virgin olive oil

sea salt and freshly ground black pepper

4 spring onions, chopped

4 tbs fresh mint, chopped

4 tbs fresh parsley, chopped

1 large vine tomato, chopped

salads

Dips

I often make one of these dips for when guests come over instead of offering crisps; serve them with sticks of carrot, celery, pepper, cucumber or fingers of wholemeal pitta bread. The children love to stay up late handing the plates around and generally feeling important. It's also a good idea to have a couple of these dips in the fridge as they are excellent for jazzing up a piece of chicken or fish, adding to salads and make for far healthier fridge raids!

Avocado dip

1 large avocado

1 large tomato

1 clove garlic

a few black pitted olives

juice of 1 lime

1 handful fresh coriander

| DF | GF | WL |

Blend the ingredients together in a food processor or with a hand blender.

Hummus

400g tinned chickpeas

1 clove garlic

sea salt

3 tbs light tahini

juice of 2 small lemons

4-5 tbs water

3 tbs extra virgin olive oil

| DF | GF | WL in moderation |

Drain and rinse the chickpeas and place in a food processor or blender.

To crush the garlic either chop the peeled cloves finely with a pinch of salt on a board or crush to a paste with the salt in a pestle and mortar.

Add the tahini, lemon juice and crushed garlic to the chickpeas and blend adding just enough water to get the right consistency. Put in a bowl and mix in the olive oil. Serve with wholemeal pitta fingers or torn pieces of flat bread (or gluten free bread).

You can be creative and add other ingredients such as pesto, fresh basil, fresh coriander, ground cumin, chilli, avocado, sliced olives... the list is endless. Nor do you have to use chickpeas: you could try making a similar dip using cannellini beans, kidney beans, butter beans, fresh hulled broad beans – just experiment!

Tapenade

150g black pitted olives

1 clove garlic

1 handful fresh basil

1 anchovy fillet

1 dsp capers, rinsed

olive oil

| DF | GF | WL |

Finely chop the olives, garlic, basil, anchovy and capers in the inner bowl of a food processor or with a hand blender, adding olive oil to loosen into a spreadable paste.

This also works really well with any fish, for example, spooned over a cod fillet and baked in the oven.

Tzatsiki

1 small cucumber

500ml thick natural live yoghurt

2 tsp fresh mint, chopped

2 garlic cloves

2 tbs olive oil

1 tbs lemon juice

sea salt and freshly ground black pepper

| GF | WL |

Grate the cucumber coarsely, and squeeze to remove the excess water.

Put the yoghurt in a bowl and stir in the mint, garlic, olive oil, lemon juice and cucumber. Season with black pepper and a little sea salt. Mix well.

This works really well with grilled meats, the Red onion salad (see page 15) and warm pitta bread.

Smoked mackerel pate/dip

200g smoked mackerel fillets, skin removed

200g cottage cheese

juice of 1 lemon

2 tbs natural yoghurt

freshly ground black pepper

| GF | WL |

Put all the ingredients into a food processor, season with pepper and blend to a smooth texture.

Serve with fingers of rye, gluten free or wholemeal pitta bread.

Soups and breads

Celeriac and rocket soup

The method of adding yoghurt to the soup might look a bit complicated but is actually really straightforward and prevents the whole thing curdling. If I am making this for friends I like to serve it with a homemade focaccia (see page 44).

Celeriac is a good source of soluble fibre which helps to lower blood cholesterol. It is also a good source of potassium which is an important mineral for lowering blood pressure, reducing the risk of stroke.

GF **WL**

Peel the celeriac, wash and cut into small cubes. Put in a large saucepan with the rocket (reserve some of the rocket for the garnish), stock, garlic and a little salt.
Bring to the boil and then simmer lightly for 25 minutes until the celeriac is tender.
At this point you may like to blitz the soup with a hand blender to a smooth consistency, although personally I like it lumpy.

Break the egg into a large mixing bowl and whisk together with the yoghurt.

Reheat the soup to boiling point, take a ladleful of the soup and whisk into the yoghurt mix, repeat until you have used half the soup and the yoghurt mix has heated up. Pour the warm yoghurt/soup mixture into the soup pan, whisking constantly. Bring back to a gentle simmer. Season, stir in the spring onions and serve garnished with rocket.

ingredients

400g celeriac

45g rocket, roughly chopped

1 litre vegetable stock
(made with reduced salt Marigold bouillon)

10 garlic cloves, chopped finely

1 organic egg

350g thick natural yoghurt

sea salt and freshly ground black pepper

6 spring onions, chopped into rings

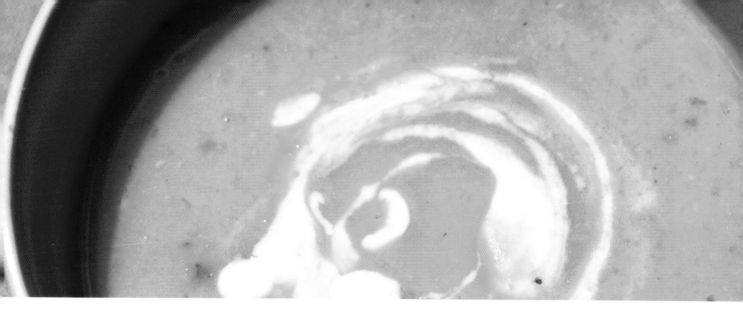

'Orange man' soup

My son, Marley, used to be obsessed with the colour orange and given the choice would only wear orange clothes. 'Orange Man' was his own superhero creation. For obvious reasons we named this soup after his superhero and still cook it regularly. It is a real winter warmer and is fantastic in mugs on Bonfire Night with a swirl of crème fraîche.

Orange coloured vegetables are a great source of beta-carotene which converts in the body to vitamin A – a very important antioxidant and immune system booster.

The beans and lentils provide plenty of protein, making this soup a complete meal in itself.

| **DF** avoid the crème fraîche | **GF** | **WL** steam fry the veggies with minimum oil and a little water |

Sauté the onion and garlic in a little olive oil. Add the squash, sweet potato and carrots and continue to sauté for a few minutes. Pour in the stock so that it just covers the vegetables, add the lentils and the herbs. Cook on a gentle heat for about 20 minutes and then add the beans. Season with black pepper. Blitz with a hand blender until smooth, adding more stock if it's too thick.

ingredients

2 medium onions, roughly sliced

3 cloves garlic, chopped

500g butternut squash, peeled and cut into chunks

500g sweet potato, peeled and cut into chunks

500g carrots, peeled and sliced roughly

1 litre vegetable stock (made with reduced salt Marigold bouillon)

100g orange lentils

1 tsp dried herbs such as sage or tarragon

400g tin cannellini beans, drained

freshly ground black pepper

Lentil and tomato soup

I love this recipe, it is full of fresh vegetables and as you eat it you know it must be doing you a whole heap of good as well as tasting divine.

We should all be eating dark green vegetables every day as they are such an important source of minerals and vitamins, I love spinach as it cooks in seconds and is equally good raw in salads – definitely one to put in your supermarket basket regularly.

DF	GF

WL a bowl of this for lunch keeps hunger at bay and is so healthy you can feel thoroughly virtuous at the same time

Heat a large pan and add 2 tbs of olive oil. Add the carrots, celery, onions and garlic and cook for approximately 10 minutes with the lid askew, until the carrots are softened.

Meanwhile peel and grate the ginger and deseed and slice the chilli finely. Add the stock to the pan with the lentils, ginger, chilli and tomatoes. Bring the soup to the boil and then reduce the heat and simmer for approximately 10 minutes with the lid on until the lentils are cooked. Add the spinach and let it wilt into the soup.

Serve immediately, seasoned with a little salt and pepper.

ingredients

2 tbs extra virgin olive oil

2 carrots, peeled and sliced

2 sticks celery, sliced

2 medium onions, peeled and chopped

2 cloves garlic, peeled and sliced

20g fresh root ginger, peeled and grated

1 fresh red chilli, deseeded and finely sliced

1.8 litres vegetable stock
(made with reduced salt Marigold bouillon)

300g red lentils

10 cherry tomatoes, halved

200g spinach, washed

sea salt and freshly ground black pepper

Roast pepper and tomato soup with butter beans

This soup takes a little time to prepare as you need to roast the peppers and tomatoes and then peel them, but it is well worth the effort. The soup is warming and delicious on a winter's day but equally good chilled as a summer soup. My advice is to make double the quantity and freeze it in portions.

Red peppers are one of the best sources of vitamin C and also beta-carotene, which makes them great immune system boosters. They are delicious roasted in this way with tomatoes and if you whiz up the flesh it makes a great sauce for chicken or white fish.

DF **GF** **WL**

Pre heat the oven to 180°C/Gas Mark 4.

Put the peppers in a large baking dish and place in the oven. After 30 minutes add the tomatoes and roast for a further 30 minutes or until the peppers are starting to blacken.

Remove the tray from the oven and tip the peppers and tomatoes into a bowl, cover with cling film to steam them. After 20 minutes the skins will peel off the peppers and tomatoes easily, discard the skins, and the seeds from the peppers, and roughly chop the flesh.

Place the tomato and pepper flesh in a saucepan with the onion and stock. Simmer for about 20 minutes until the onion is soft and then add the butter beans and fresh herbs. Blitz the soup with a hand blender until smooth and season well.

ingredients

4 red peppers

6 large tomatoes

1 large red onion, sliced

800ml vegetable stock
(made with reduced salt Marigold bouillon)

400g tinned butter beans, rinsed and drained

1 handful fresh coriander

1 handful fresh basil

sea salt and freshly ground black pepper

Tom Yum soup with prawns

I love to make this soup when I am pushed for time as it tastes amazing and is so quick to prepare. It is light and fragrant and also works well as a dinner party starter.

Xylitol is perfect here as it gives the sweetness that Thai food requires. Dried lime leaves are widely available but I also buy them frozen from my local Thai supermarket.

If I am making this for lunch I will often add buckwheat noodles to make the soup more filling. Avoid the noodles becoming mushy by cooking them separately. Slightly undercook them then run under cold water before putting them in the bottom of each bowl – the hot broth will reheat them to perfection.

Prawns are an excellent source of protein and are rich in minerals. They can be defrosted quickly and easily in a bowl of cold water, so make sure you have a supply in the freezer.

DF

GF buckwheat noodles are only gluten free if they are 100% buckwheat, read the label as wheat is often added. Most good health food shops sell 100% buckwheat noodles

WL perfect if you are watching your weight as this soup fills and satisfies whilst being low in fat and starchy carbs

Heat the stock in a large pan and add the lemongrass, ripped lime leaves, chilli, ginger, fish sauce and xylitol. Bring to the boil, then reduce heat to the lowest setting and leave to infuse for 10 minutes. Drop the prawns into the broth and cook for a couple of minutes. Distribute the coriander and basil among six bowls. Squeeze a little lime juice over the top and pour in the soup. Serve with a wedge of lime.

ingredients

1 litre vegetable stock
(made with reduced salt Marigold bouillon)

6 small sticks lemongrass

12 lime leaves, ripped

1 fresh red chilli, deseeded and finely sliced

20g fresh root ginger, thinly sliced

2 tbs fish sauce

10g xylitol (natural sugar alternative)

200g raw tiger prawns,
gutted and split in half

1 handful coriander leaves

1 handful basil leaves

juice of 2 limes

1 lime, cut into 6 wedges

Thai coconut soup

This is always a favourite at my cookery workshops, I make it as soon as everyone arrives as they are usually starving and this is so quick and simple to make.

An authentic Thai soup would use palm sugar for sweetness but I have replaced it with xylitol as a healthier alternative. Galangal would also be used traditionally, but if you can't find it I find that ginger works just as well. Lemongrass is sold in good supermarkets but I tend to buy it in larger quantities at the Thai supermarket and freeze it.

| DF | GF | WL |

Place the sliced ginger/galangal and lemongrass in a heavy based pan with the coconut milk, tamari soy sauce and xylitol.

Bring to the boil and simmer for 10 minutes, stirring occasionally. Add the mushrooms and vegetables, return to the boil and simmer for a further 3 minutes. Season if necessary with a little more soy sauce or xylitol.

Ladle the soup into bowls and serve topped with fresh coriander leaves.

ingredients

25g fresh root ginger or galangal, peeled and sliced

2 lemongrass stalks, sliced

2 x 400ml tins low fat coconut milk

2 tbs tamari soy sauce

1 dsp xylitol (natural sugar alternative)

150g mushrooms, sliced

400g mixed vegetables, sliced: sugar snap peas, mange tout, baby sweetcorn, red peppers

fresh coriander leaves to garnish

Chicken noodle soup

This is a really quick and easy lunch or supper, and a soup that my children love too. I grate the ginger to prevent anyone getting a big mouthful of it, or chop it finely. This is a child-friendly version but you can add a finely chopped red chilli if you want more heat.

To prevent soggy noodles cook them separately and rinse under cold water. When ready to serve, place the noodles in the bottom of each bowl and then top with the soup which reheats them perfectly.

You don't have to use these vegetables, use whatever you have to hand, for example, broccoli cut into tiny florets would work well as would mange tout or sugar snap peas.

DF GF WL

Bring the stock to the boil in a large saucepan and add the soy sauce, black pepper and ginger. Cover and simmer for approximately 5 minutes.

Add the chicken slices and simmer for a further few minutes. Add the mushrooms, carrots and courgette slices and simmer for a couple more minutes until the chicken is tender. Add the rice noodles and just before they are cooked add the spinach.

Serve in bowls and sprinkle with the spring onions, sesame seeds and coriander leaves.

ingredients

1.8 litres vegetable stock
(made with reduced salt Marigold bouillon)

1 tbs tamari soy sauce

½ tsp freshly ground black pepper

20g fresh root ginger, peeled and grated

2 chicken breasts, cut into thin slices

100g mushrooms, sliced

2 carrots, cut into thin batons

1 courgette, sliced

3 bunches of rice noodles (180g)

100g spinach

2 spring onions, cut into small rounds

2 tsp sesame seeds

1 bunch coriander leaves

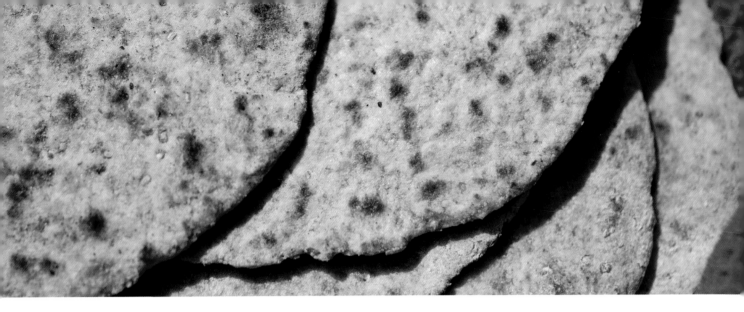

Wholemeal roti

These are easy to make and yeast free – so you don't have to wait around for hours for the dough to rise. I like to make these whenever I am making an Indian dish as they are great for mopping up curry or dahl, and the puffing up over the gas flame is quite exciting!

DF

GF you can use the Doves Farm brown bread flour but will need to eat the rotis quickly as they tend to go a bit leathery and stiff if left for any time

ingredients

300g chapatti flour, or wholewheat flour

150ml warm water

1-2 tbs olive oil

Sift the flour into a bowl and make a well in the centre. Slowly drizzle in 150ml of warm water and the oil, mix well. The dough should feel slightly sticky.

Knead the dough for 10 minutes, place in a bowl and cover with a damp tea towel. Leave in a warm place for 30 minutes.

Divide the dough into 12 equal portions and roll into golf-sized balls in your hands. Dust the work surface and roll each ball into a thin circle about 15cm across.

Heat a non-stick frying pan until quite hot. Place a dough circle in the pan, reduce the heat and cook until small bubbles appear on the underside, then turn. Cook the other side until the base has small dark spots.

Puff each roti by holding over a gas flame with tongs, or if you have an electric hob by pressing down in the pan one side at a time. Keep the roti warm by wrapping them in foil and keeping in a low oven until they all are cooked.

Spicy corn bread

This is a winning recipe as it is impressively quick to make and is wonderful with soup. My Sainsbury's stocks the cornmeal in the 'World food' section – alongside all the lovely Indian spices.

DF you could use coconut oil in place of butter if you don't mind a slight coconut flavour, and use soya milk rather than cow's

GF use Doves Farm gluten free brown bread flour in place of wholemeal flour

Preheat the oven to 200°C/Gas Mark 6. Butter a 22cm square brownie tin, dust with flour.

Melt the butter and leave to cool a little.

Mix the cornmeal with the flour, baking powder, chopped chilli and salt.

Stir in the spring onions. Whisk the melted butter with the milk and eggs. Mix everything together, pour the mixture into the tin and bake for about 35 minutes.

ingredients

100g butter

180g fine cornmeal

180g wholemeal flour

2 tsp baking powder

1 red chilli, deseeded and chopped finely

1 tsp salt

6 spring onions, chopped

460ml milk

2 eggs

Foccacia

Focaccia is easy to make but you need to start a good few hours before you intend to eat it as the dough needs time to rise. If you are having friends over for supper it is very impressive served on a wooden board alongside bowls of steaming soup. Let your guests tear off hunks of the bread with their hands – they'll love it!

You can choose whatever topping you like – I like to choose from pitted black olives, goat's cheese, basil, sundried tomatoes, parsley... it all works.

DF

GF I have tried this recipe with Doves Farm gluten free brown bread flour and it works reasonably well although it does not have quite the same doughiness

Put the yeast and water in a large mixing bowl and stir until the yeast dissolves. Add half of the flour and stir until you get a porridgy consistency. Cover the bowl with a damp cloth and leave in a warm place for a couple of hours to double in size.

Mix in the rest of the flour, sugar and olive oil. Stir with a wooden spoon until the mixture comes together. Knead for a good 5 minutes, add the salt and continue to knead for another couple of minutes until the salt is thoroughly incorporated and the dough is elastic.

Brush a large bowl with olive oil, place the dough in the bowl and brush with more oil. Cover the dough with the damp cloth and leave again in a warm place for about an hour, until doubled in size.

On a floured surface work the dough into a rectangle. Take one short edge and fold into the centre. Take the other end and fold over the first, to make 3 layers of dough.

Take a heavy baking tray about 30cm x 40cm and brush with oil. Lift the dough onto the tray so that the seam is on the bottom. Flatten the dough onto the tray. Cover with cling film and leave to rise for another hour. During this time gradually work the dough towards the corners of the tray every 15 minutes or so, until it covers the whole tray – and is about 2cm thick.

Preheat the oven to 220°C/Gas Mark 7. Put your choice of topping on the focaccia, for example, chopped parsley, olives and sea salt. Place the focaccia in the oven for 10 minutes then reduce the temperature to 190°C/Gas Mark 5 and continue to cook for another 20 minutes. When out of the oven and still hot brush with plenty of olive oil.

Serves six generously.

ingredients

1½ tsp active dried yeast
(I use Hovis as it comes in handy sachets)

420ml lukewarm filtered water

660g strong wholemeal flour

1 tbs light brown sugar

2 tbs olive oil

1 tbs sea salt

choice of toppings

soups and breads

Veggie options and sides

Puy lentils with tomatoes and herbs

Lentils have had a bad press, but this is unfair as they are really delicious if cooked in tasty stock with onion, garlic and plenty of herbs. Forget the association with hippies in floaty robes and sandals, you will be proud to serve these lentils at a dinner party or at any weekday meal, they are simple to make and a great alternative to rice and potatoes. In place of herbs you might like to wilt spinach into the cooked lentils, I also sometimes swirl in some natural yoghurt at the end.

Lentils are mostly made up of starchy carbs and a fistful is therefore all you need as a portion on the plate. They are a useful source of protein as well as providing slow release carbohydrate and are therefore a good food for keeping blood sugar levels stable.

| DF | GF | WL steam fry the veggies with minimum oil and a little water |

In a heavy-based saucepan sauté the chopped onion, garlic and celery in olive oil. You can also add one chopped deseeded chilli if you want this dish to have more of a bite. When the onions are soft add the lentils and stir for one minute.

Add enough stock to just cover and leave to simmer. Check occasionally, adding more stock as necessary so that lentils do not stick to the base of the saucepan. It should take about 25 minutes for the lentils to soften. Once you are happy that the lentils are cooked, add the tomatoes and herbs, stir through with the lemon juice and an extra glug of olive oil. Season with pepper.

ingredients

1 red onion, chopped

1 red chilli, deseeded and finely chopped

3 cloves garlic, crushed

2 stalks of celery, chopped

olive oil

250g puy lentils

600ml vegetable stock
(made with reduced salt Marigold bouillon)

2 medium ripe tomatoes, chopped

fresh herbs, chopped – dill, basil, coriander

juice of ½ lemon

freshly ground black pepper

Butter bean bake

This dish is always popular at my vegetarian cookery workshops, it is a doddle to make and an easy way to include pulses – I know those tins of beans can sit idle in the cupboard for months! To increase the protein for vegetarians you could serve this with a small dish of feta, otherwise it goes excellently with grilled chicken.

Butter beans are a very good source of cholesterol-lowering fibre, as are most other legumes. In addition to lowering cholesterol, the high fibre content prevents blood sugar levels from rising too rapidly after a meal, and they therefore help to maintain stable energy levels.

| **DF** | **GF** | **WL** steam fry the onions with minimum oil and a little water |

Heat the olive oil in a large frying pan. Gently sauté the onions, take off the heat and add the celery, garlic, tomatoes, parsley, bay leaf and beans. Season with black pepper and a little sea salt. Pour the mixture into a baking dish. Cover with foil and bake in the oven for approximately 30 minutes. Serve warm with a drizzle of olive oil.

ingredients

2 tbs olive oil

2 small red onions, finely chopped

2 celery stalks with leaves, chopped

3 garlic cloves, finely chopped

650g tinned tomatoes

4 tbs parsley, chopped

1 bay leaf

400g tinned butter beans, rinsed and drained

Roasted vegetables with feta cheese

This is a lovely way to cook vegetables and really easy, especially if someone helps you with the chopping. Make plenty as the vegetables are lovely cold the next day.

Research on aubergines has focused on an anthocyanin phytonutrient found in the skin called nasunin. Nasunin is a potent antioxidant and free radical scavenger that has been shown to protect cell membranes from damage.

GF	**WL** use a pastry brush to brush olive oil over the vegetables rather than tossing them in oil

Heat the oven to 190°C/Gas Mark 5.

Chop the vegetables into large chunks, leave the garlic cloves whole.

Pour the olive oil into a roasting pan with the salt, pepper, rosemary and thyme. Toss the vegetables in the seasoned oil making sure they are evenly covered and place into the oven. After about 20 minutes re-toss the vegetables and put back in the oven for a further 20-25 minutes.

Finally add some cubes of feta and put back into the oven for a few minutes. Once out of the oven, drizzle with some Harissa sauce (see next recipe). This goes excellently with some quinoa cooked in stock.

ingredients

1 red pepper

1 yellow pepper

200g courgettes

200g aubergine

100g mushrooms

200g cherry tomatoes

2 small red onions

10 garlic cloves, peeled

5 tbs olive oil

sea salt and freshly ground black pepper

fresh or dried rosemary and thyme

100g feta cubes

Harissa sauce

I once read an interview with Nigella Lawson and she said that if she were stranded on a desert island and only allowed one luxury it would be Harissa sauce – it really brings vegetables and grilled meats to life, so it's a good idea to keep some in the fridge at all times. Beluza do a lovely one made with rose petals if you prefer to buy it ready made.

Mix all the ingredients together – that simple!

ingredients

3 tbs olive oil

½ tsp cayenne pepper
(more if you like more of a kick)

1 tbs cumin

1 tbs tomato purée

juice of 1 lime

Sushi rolls

This is a great way to get people eating more nori seaweed, which is one of the best sources of iodine, a mineral crucial for thyroid health that many of us are deficient in. This is why a little sea salt in your cooking is also a good idea, as it is also rich in iodine.

My children love to help assemble these. I sometimes make the rolls and then cut them into three to serve with drinks. They make a great starter with the Fresh spring rolls (see next recipe).

Short grain brown rice works well for the sushi as it seems to be stickier than brown basmati rice, however, inevitably, some will drop out as you eat the sushi so watch out! Feel free to experiment with the filling, I have been very adventurous in the past using cold omelette, poached salmon, tuna, prawns – anything you fancy – within reason!

A sushi mat is useful but not essential.

Cook the rice and allow to cool. When the rice has cooled add the brown rice vinegar.

Lay a sheet of nori on the sushi mat. Arrange a layer of rice in a square on the nori leaving a good border all around the rice. Across the middle lay thin strips of spring onion, smoked salmon, carrot, cucumber, avocado and ginger. Wet the free edge of the nori and carefully roll the whole lot tightly into a roll. Leave in the fridge for 30 minutes to set. You can slice each roll into three or four pieces and can serve with wasabi paste and pickled ginger (both available from an Asian supermarket) and tamari soy sauce.

ingredients

200g cooked short grain brown rice (makes five generous rolls)

1 tsp Japanese brown rice vinegar

5 sheets nori seaweed

3 spring onions, finely cut lengthwise

2 large slices smoked salmon, cut into strips

2 carrots, finely cut lengthways

¼ cucumber, sliced into matchstick-thin strips

1 avocado, cut into long strips

10g fresh root ginger, cut into long, thin matchsticks

tamari soy sauce (for dipping)

Fresh spring rolls

This is one of my favourite dishes at our local Thai restaurant, Budsara, in Chiswick. The lovely owner always gives me a container of her homemade sweet chilli sauce for my cookery workshops but you can buy Thai sweet chilli dipping sauce at most good supermarkets – use with caution as it is full of sugar!

These spring rolls are packed with fresh vegetables and are eaten raw rather than deep fried. Stuff them with whatever filling you fancy; another option could be poached salmon and avocado with spring onion and pepper strips. Use whatever you have in the salad box for a quick and easy lunch. If you are making them in advance cover with a damp tea towel to prevent the rice wrappers from drying out.

| DF | GF |

WL make an alternative sugar-free dipping sauce by combining tamari soy sauce with a finely chopped chilli, lime juice and a little xylitol

Marinate the prawns in the chilli, soy sauce, lime juice, ginger and garlic for at least 10 minutes, place in a food processor and mince the ingredients (or use the prawns whole if you prefer).

Soak the rice paper wrapper in warm water for about 20 seconds. Place on a damp tea towel and place a couple of teaspoons of minced prawns and a little of each of the other ingredients in the middle of the wrapper. Fold into a packet/parcel. Make a couple of parcels per person and serve immediately with a dipping sauce.

ingredients

200g frozen cooked prawns, defrosted

1 chilli, chopped and deseeded

2 tsp tamari soy sauce

juice of 1 lime

20g fresh root ginger, grated

2 garlic cloves, chopped finely

1 packet of rice wrappers

3 carrots, cut into strips

3 spring onions, cut into strips

¼ Chinese leaf lettuce, chopped

1 large handful mint leaves

1 large handful basil and coriander leaves

½ yellow pepper, cut into strips

½ red pepper, cut into strips

Ginger broccoli

Broccoli is a superfood and we all know we should be eating plenty of it, but it can get just a bit boring. Once you have cooked broccoli this way you will never look back, the children love it too.

Broccoli belongs to the cruciferous family of vegetables along with cabbage, cauliflower and Brussels sprouts. It contains cancer protective compounds and is rich in both vitamin A and C, so a good source of antioxidants.

DF **GF** **WL**

Heat the olive oil in a heavy-based frying pan or wok. Add the broccoli and toss with a pair of tongs for a couple of minutes until the broccoli turns a darker shade of emerald green.

Add the ginger and sesame seeds and continue to cook for a minute.

Add the soy sauce, fish sauce, sesame oil and water and cover so that the broccoli continues to steam fry for a minute until cooked.

ingredients

1 tbs olive oil

1 large head broccoli, cut into florets

20g fresh root ginger, grated

3 tsp sesame seeds

1 tsp tamari soy sauce

1 tsp fish sauce

1 tsp sesame oil

3 tbs water

Tarka Dahl

Tarka Dahl is a real favourite of mine, it goes so well with the Easy chicken curry (see page 72) and because the lentils are predominantly starch you won't need to cook rice too. Make plenty and freeze some if you are feeling extra efficient.

Try and include turmeric in your diet whenever possible as it is renowned for its anti-inflammatory properties. Curcumin is thought to be the primary pharmacological agent in turmeric. In numerous studies, curcumin's anti-inflammatory effects have been shown to be comparable to hydrocortisone as well as over-the-counter anti-inflammatory medicine. Unlike the drugs, which are associated with significant toxic effects (ulcer formation, decreased white blood cell count, intestinal bleeding) curcumin produces no toxicity.

DF **GF** **WL**

Place the lentils and 1 litre of water in a deep saucepan. Bring to the boil and skim off any froth. Cover and simmer for about 20 minutes adding more water if necessary.

Meanwhile, heat the oil in a small saucepan, add the cumin seeds and cook for a minute and then add the onion, chillies and ginger and cook for about 10 minutes until golden.

Purée the garlic and tomatoes in a blender, add to the onion mixture with the salt, powdered spices and 100ml water. Cook for about 15 minutes over a moderate heat.

Stir into the cooked lentils, add more water if it's too thick. Bring to the boil, stir in the fresh coriander and serve.

ingredients

250g red lentils, rinsed

2 tbs olive oil

1 tbs cumin seeds

1 small onion, peeled and chopped

3-4 green chillies, slit

20g fresh root ginger, peeled and cut into thin strips

2 large cloves garlic, peeled

3 large tomatoes

sea salt

1 tsp turmeric

1 tsp garam masala

1½ tsp ground coriander

1 handful fresh coriander leaves and stalks, chopped

Spinach and coconut dahl

The first time I made this dahl I used 1 litre of water and the consistency was very soupy but equally delicious if soupiness is what you want.

Yellow split peas are found on the supermarket shelves next to the lentils, they are also sold as Chana Dal in the Indian section of the supermarket. Dried peas are a good source of soluble fibre – important for escorting excess cholesterol out of the body.

Split peas also contain isoflavones (notably daidzein). Isoflavones are phytonutrients that can act like weak estrogens in the body and whose dietary consumption has been linked to a reduced risk of certain health conditions, including breast and prostate cancer.

| DF | GF |

WL sauté the mustard seeds and onion in coconut oil as this oil is made up of medium chain triglycerides which are more likely to go to be used for energy rather than stored as fat

Bring the peas, turmeric, cumin seeds and chillies to the boil in a saucepan with 700ml of water. Cover and reduce heat to low simmer for 40 minutes until the peas are tender. Cook the mustard seeds in the oil in a small frying pan until they pop, add the onion and fry gently. Stir in the garlic to soften. Pour the onion mixture into the peas with the salt and the coconut milk, stir well, top with spinach and stir again until the spinach wilts into the dahl.

ingredients

225g yellow split peas

½ tsp ground turmeric

½ tsp cumin seeds

3 green chillies, split lengthways, seeds removed

700ml water

1 tsp black mustard seeds

2 tbs olive oil or coconut oil

1 small onion, finely sliced

3 garlic cloves, finely chopped

1 tsp sea salt

400ml low fat coconut milk

225g spinach, shredded

Spicy cucumber and peas

Cooked cucumber is a weird concept – I've had people at my cookery workshops feeling rather doubtful about the idea, but it really works and everyone loves it. This is a great side dish to serve with any Indian style curry, it adds a cool freshness to the meal and is also dead easy – ready in minutes.

Cucumber's high water content makes it naturally hydrating – a must for glowing skin. Two compounds in cucumbers, ascorbic acid and caffeic acid, prevent water retention, which may explain why cucumbers applied topically are often helpful for puffy eyes, burns and dermatitis.

| GF | WL | use 1 tsp of olive oil with a little water to steam fry the ingredients |

To prepare the cucumber peel it first, then slice lengthways and scoop out the seeds with a teaspoon. Slice across the two lengths to make half moons.

Heat the oil in a small saucepan and add the cumin and mustard seeds. Once they start to pop add the remaining spices, a little salt and the cucumber. Cook over a medium heat for about 5 minutes. Add the peas and cook for a couple more minutes. Stir in the yoghurt and mint, heat through and serve.

ingredients

1½ tbs olive oil

1 tsp cumin seeds

½ tsp mustard seeds

½ tsp turmeric

¼ tsp chilli powder

1 tsp ground coriander

sea salt

1 medium cucumber, peeled and sliced

120g frozen peas

3 rounded tbs natural yoghurt

1 handful fresh mint leaves, shredded

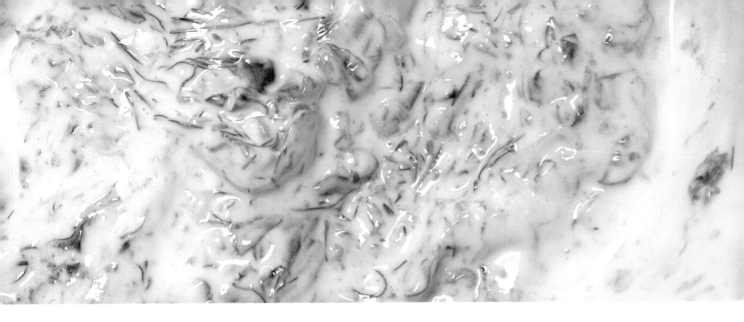

Spinach and dill raita

This goes amazingly well with any curry or dahl – in fact I love it so much I can't eat Indian food without it.

Spinach is good for cardiovascular health as it is an excellent source of folic acid. Folic acid is needed by the body to help convert a potentially dangerous chemical called homocysteine into other benign molecules. If homocysteine gets too high it can lead to a heart attack or a stroke. In addition, spinach is an excellent source of magnesium, a mineral that can help to lower high blood pressure and protect against heart disease.

GF | WL

Place the spinach and dill in a saucepan with a little water and cook for a couple of minutes, drain and run under cold water. Squeeze out any excess water and finely shred. Stir the shredded spinach and dill into the yoghurt with the salt, pepper and ground cumin.

ingredients

100g baby spinach, washed

1 handful of dill sprigs

500ml natural yoghurt

sea salt and freshly ground black pepper

1 tsp ground cumin

Vegetable frittata

A frittata is a great way to use up what's in the veggie box – as long as you have eggs you will always be able to make some version of this for supper. The classic Spanish 'tortilla' uses cooked sliced potato but to maximise your nutrient intake use tomatoes, peppers, courgettes…

Many of my clients are afraid of eating eggs as they have a reputation for raising cholesterol, yet there have been numerous studies which show that this is not the case. Studies have found no significant differences between blood levels of total, HDL and LDL cholesterol, and triglycerides in non-egg and egg eating groups.

Healthy people can safely enjoy eggs without increasing their heart attack risk.

| DF | GF | WL |

Heat the oven to 180°C/Gas Mark 4.

Put the tomatoes in a baking dish with the whole garlic cloves and basil, brush with olive oil and roast in the oven for approximately 30 minutes.

Meanwhile steam fry the onion rings using a tiny amount of olive oil and water/stock, over a medium heat.

Add the roasted tomatoes and garlic to the onions, then cover the vegetables with the beaten eggs. Cook over a medium heat until set on the bottom, then place under a medium grill to cook the top of the tortilla.

Serve warm or leave to get cold, and cut into slices. Serve with a big green salad.

ingredients

300g cherry tomatoes

6 garlic cloves, peeled

1 handful basil

2 medium-sized onions, cut into rings

olive oil

water/stock

8 beaten eggs

Sesame tofu with steam-fried vegetables

Veggie options and sides

For main courses I like to cook chicken, turkey or fish but sometimes I feel the need for a break from these and will use tofu as my source of protein. This recipe is great if you are 'detoxing' and being uber healthy.

Soy has been shown to be helpful in alleviating the symptoms associated with menopause. Soy foods, like tofu, contain phytoestrogens, and in a woman's body these compounds can dock at estrogen receptors and act like very, very weak estrogens. During perimenopause, when a woman's estrogen fluctuates, soy's phytoestrogens can help her maintain balance, blocking out estrogen when levels rise excessively high, plus filling in for estrogen when levels are low. When women's production of natural estrogen drops at menopause, the phytoestrogens in soy may provide just enough estrogenic activity to prevent or reduce uncomfortable symptoms, like hot flushes.

Soy needs to be eaten in moderation, like it is in Asia where it has been linked with promoting health. In Japan, for example, individuals seldom consume large quantities of soy at one time. When soy foods are consumed, traditionally fermented soy products like fermented tofu, fermented miso and fermented soy sauce are best when it comes to our health.

DF | **GF** | **WL**

Chop the tofu into cubes. If you prefer a firmer texture then place in a colander, cover with a plate and place a heavy object (such as a filled kettle) on top, leave for about 20 minutes. This squeezes excess water from the tofu.

Heat 1 teaspoon of olive oil in a wok or large frying pan and add a little water to steam fry the tofu cubes until golden brown. Place the cooked pieces onto kitchen roll to blot any excess oil then toss in sesame seeds, sesame oil and tamari soy sauce.

Heat another teaspoon of olive oil in the heavy-based frying pan and quickly stir in the onion and garlic. Add the stock and continue to cook gently. When the onions are soft add the vegetables, apart from the spinach. Cover with a tight-fitting lid and turn the heat down.

The vegetables will cook in the heat of the steam. (If you don't have a lid this method will still work but will take slightly longer.) Leave for about 5 minutes and at the last minute add the spinach (if using). Season with freshly ground black pepper, sea salt and chopped coriander. You may like to add a few drops of tamari soy sauce in place of salt. Serve the vegetables topped with the Sesame tofu.

ingredients

for the sesame tofu

1 packet plain tofu

1 tsp olive oil

1 tbs sesame seeds

1 tsp sesame oil

1 tsp tamari soy sauce

for the steam-fried vegetables

1 tsp olive oil

1 medium-sized onion, chopped

3 cloves of garlic, chopped

¼ litre vegetable stock (made with reduced salt Marigold bouillon)

800g of chopped seasonal vegetables: carrots, courgettes, peppers, cherry tomatoes, spinach or pak choi, broccoli…

sea salt and freshly ground black pepper

1 handful coriander, chopped

Rice

Brown basmati rice has the lowest glycaemic index of all rice which means it helps to maintain good energy levels and keeps you feeling fuller for longer. The fibre in brown rice is where all the goodness is, refining it to white strips rice of its valuable nutrients. That's all very well but many people think brown rice is boring, so here are some good ideas for turning it into something delicious.

Macro rice

This is my mum's favourite, we have been making it since the 80s when we got into healthy eating!

200g brown basmati rice, washed and drained

2 tbs olive oil

1 medium onion, chopped finely

2 cloves garlic, chopped finely

1 large handful flat leaf parsley, chopped

tamari soy sauce

DF	GF

WL steam fry the onion and garlic with minimum oil and a little water

Cook the rice in plenty of boiling water and drain.

Sauté the onion and garlic in the olive oil.

Combine the onion and garlic with the cooked rice and the parsley.

Sprinkle with tamari soy sauce.

Saffron rice

2 tbs olive oil

1 tsp cumin seeds

½ cinnamon stick

3 cloves

3 green cardamom pods

1 bay leaf

1 medium onion, peeled and sliced finely

200g brown basmati rice, washed and drained

400ml water

1 good pinch of saffron strands, soaked in 2 tbs hot milk

sea salt

15g pistachios

DF soak saffron in 2 tbs hot water | **GF**

WL steam fry the spices with minimum oil and a little water

Heat the oil in a large saucepan. Add the whole spices and bay leaf and cook over a low heat for 30 seconds. Add the onion and cook until soft and golden.

Add the washed and drained rice to the pan, stir into the spiced oil and then add 400ml water, the soaked saffron and the milk and a little salt. Bring to the boil, then reduce heat to a low setting and cover. Cook for 25 minutes until the rice is tender. Add the pistachios and serve hot.

Lime and coriander rice

200g brown basmati rice, washed and drained

1 large bunch coriander, leaves removed and chopped

2 limes, zested and halved

olive oil

sea salt and freshly ground black pepper

DF | **GF** | **WL**

Cook the rice in plenty of boiling water and drain.

Mix the coriander and lime zest into the freshly cooked brown basmati rice, squeeze over the lime juice. Drizzle with a little olive oil, season with salt and pepper and stir well.

Mains

Goan prawn curry

This curry is quick and easy and thoroughly delicious. Use coconut butter if you have it to increase the coconut flavour.

Prawns are rich in protein and zinc, an essential mineral for building and maintaining a healthy immune system. Zinc is also good for sexual development, the nervous system and brain function. There is evidence that people who suffer from low zinc levels have a poor libido – another reason to pop a prawn or two.

DF **GF** **WL**

Heat the oil/coconut butter in a large pan and add the mustard seeds. Stir continuously until you hear the mustard seeds start to pop. Add the onion, garlic, ginger and chilli and fry until soft.

Add the cumin, coriander, paprika, turmeric and salt and stir well.

Add the tomatoes, coconut milk and lemon juice and bring to the boil, simmer gently for 15 minutes.

Add the prawns to heat through if pre-cooked, or cook for a few minutes until they turn pink if using raw prawns.

Serve with saffron rice/basmati rice and fresh coriander.

ingredients

1 tbs oil/coconut butter

½ tsp black mustard seeds

1 large onion, chopped

2 cloves garlic, finely chopped

20g fresh root ginger, finely chopped

1 red chilli, deseeded and roughly chopped

1 tsp ground cumin

1 tsp ground coriander

1 tsp paprika

½ tsp turmeric

½ tsp salt

4 large tomatoes, finely chopped

400ml low fat coconut milk

juice of ½ lemon

450g cooked or raw king prawns, peeled

mains

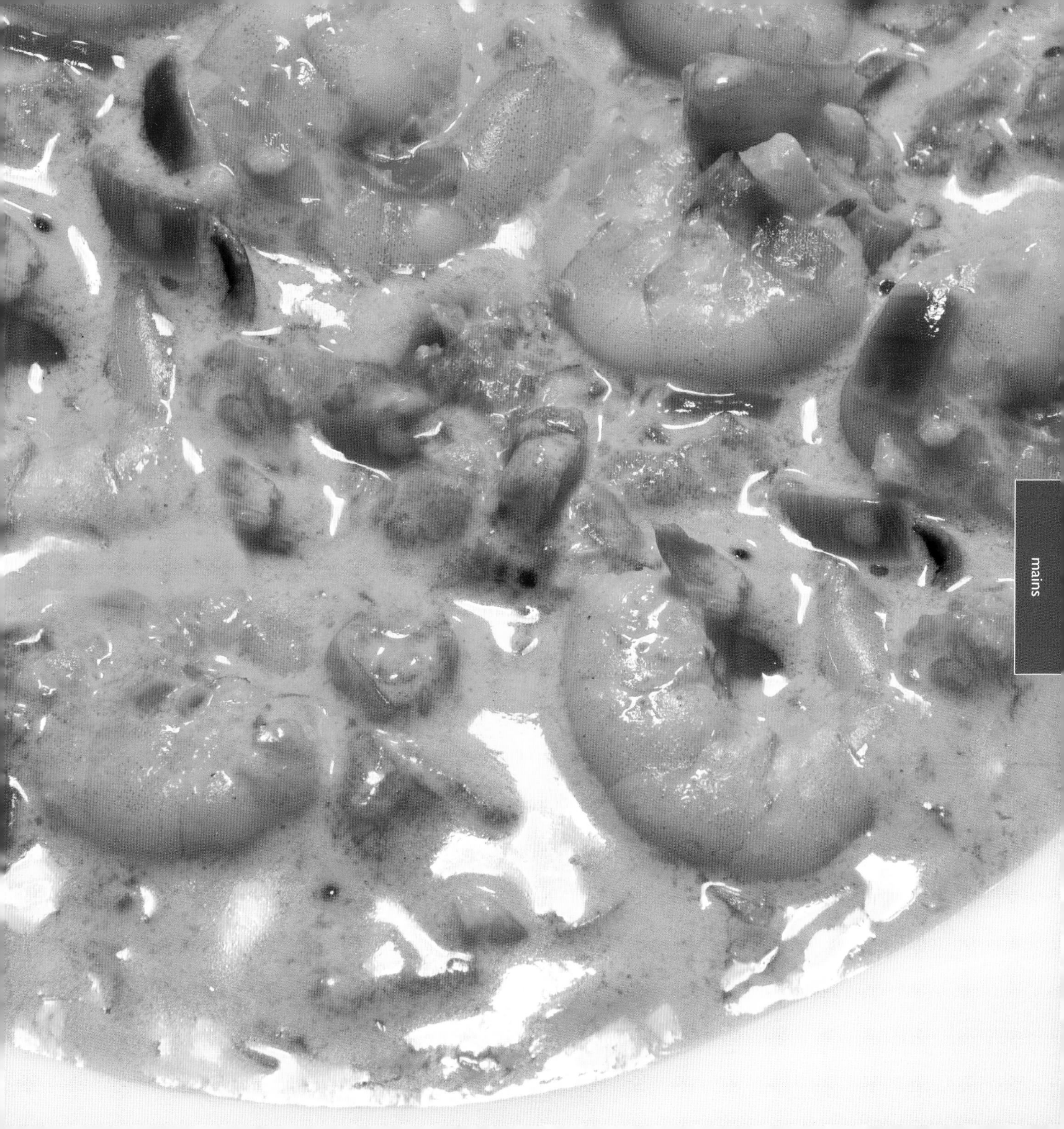

Salmon curry in a wrap

This is a family favourite. I put the curry, lettuce and raita out in bowls as the children love to assemble their own wraps. At my workshops people are surprised at how much they love this recipe as many have never thought of fish and curry as natural partners.

Salmon is rich in omega 3 essential fats, which are crucial for so many functions in the body. They are, for example, important for good cardiovascular health, for mental health and for keeping blood sugar levels stable.

I use organic, virgin coconut butter for this dish as it is one of the healthiest fats to cook with, and the coconut flavour goes perfectly with the salmon giving it a healthy korma-like taste.

DF avoid the raita | **GF** if you are avoiding gluten serve this curry with rice or use corn tortillas

WL if you are reducing fat in your diet, use only a teaspoon of the coconut butter with water to steam fry

Heat the oil or coconut butter in a large heavy-based pan and add the mustard seeds. Once the seeds are popping add the onion and fry until lightly coloured – about 8 minutes. Add the ginger, chilli, garlic and curry leaves and fry briefly. Stir in the powdered spices and salt. Add the tomatoes, coconut and 200ml water. Bring to the boil and cover, cook for about 10 minutes. Add the lemon juice.

Add the salmon and cook over a low heat, flaking up the salmon to speed up the cooking.

Put some of the salmon curry along the centre of a tortilla or roti, add lettuce and raita and roll – prepare for messy eating as the juice will run out. Not one for a first date!

ingredients

2 tbs coconut butter

½ tsp mustard seeds

1 small onion, peeled and finely chopped

10g fresh root ginger, peeled and finely chopped

1 red chilli, chopped finely

2 large cloves garlic, peeled and finely chopped

8 curry leaves

1½ tsp ground coriander

¼ tsp turmeric

1 tsp garam masala

½ tsp sea salt

3 large tomatoes, chopped

60g desiccated coconut

200ml water

1 tsp lemon juice

300g salmon fillets, skinless and boneless

wholewheat tortillas or roti (see page 44)

Iceberg or Romaine lettuce, shredded

raita (see page 62)

Easy chicken curry

This curry is so easy to make you will be amazed! All you need is fresh chicken and some store cupboard and fridge basics and you can produce your own aromatic curry in just 15 minutes. At my cookery workshops this always gets a massive thumbs-up.

Include turmeric in your diet as it has fantastic anti-inflammatory properties. Anyone with arthritis should make it a staple. I always buy the large packets in the Indian section of the supermarket as I use it all the time.

DF avoid yoghurt/raita	**GF**
WL steam fry the onion, chilli, garlic and chicken with minimum oil and a little water	

Heat the oil in a heavy-based frying pan, then fry the onion, chilli and garlic for a few minutes, add the chicken pieces and continue to fry for about 5 minutes. When the mixture begins to brown add the salt, turmeric, cumin and coriander to the chicken mixture. Stir well and continue to fry. Add the tomato purée and garam masala.

If you like you could add some chopped tomatoes or other vegetables to the chicken. You could also stir in some natural yoghurt at the end if you are not serving with a raita (see Spinach and dill raita page 60).

ingredients

4 tbs olive oil

2 medium onions, peeled and sliced

2 green chillies, seeded and chopped

3 cloves garlic, crushed and chopped

3-4 chicken breasts, skinned and chopped into bite-sized pieces

½ tsp sea salt

½ tsp turmeric

1 tsp ground cumin seeds

½ tsp ground coriander seeds

2 tbs tomato purée

½ tsp garam masala

mains

Roast chicken masala

This is one of Mr Tailor's recipes – a lovely Indian gentleman who I met at the Asian Centre in Wood Green. I was brought in to teach a healthy eating class, and was really impressed by the group's own favourite recipes.

Skinless, boneless chicken thigh pieces work well – the meat is really tasty and cheaper than buying chicken breast. I have slightly adapted this recipe – Mr Tailor uses 6 chillies!

If I have time I like to cover the chicken in the paste and leave it in the fridge for a couple of hours so that all the lovely flavours really seep into the chicken. However, more often than not I put it straight into the oven and it still tastes amazing.

Research suggests that the volatile oils found in the leaves of the coriander plant may have antimicrobial properties. Coriander leaves like all dark leaves are also a good source of minerals and vitamins.

Put all the ingredients, except the chicken, in a food processor and blend to a paste. Cover the chicken in the paste in a shallow ovenproof dish and refrigerate for a couple of hours – time permitting.

Bake in the oven for 20 minutes until the chicken is cooked through. Serve with a crunchy mixed salad and some saffron rice.

ingredients

2 skinless chicken breasts, sliced into smaller fillets; or 4 chicken thighs, boneless and skinless

1 green chilli, deseeded

20g fresh root ginger, peeled

4 cloves garlic, peeled

1 tsp cumin seeds

1 tsp coriander seeds

1 tbs lemon juice

½ tsp garam masala

2 tbs olive oil

1 tsp sea salt

1 bunch fresh coriander (30g)

Salmon ceviche

This is ideal if you are not in the mood for cooking – the lime juice cooks the salmon for you!

Remove any bones from the salmon fillet, slice into small strips no thicker than half a centimetre and put into a shallow non-metallic dish.

Pour the lime juice, chilli, coriander, cumin and garlic over the fish and season with a little black pepper and sea salt. Squeeze the grated ginger over the fish discarding the pulp. Mix through gently, cover with cling film and leave in the fridge to 'cook' for at least 2 hours before serving.

A quicker alternative, if you are short for time, is to use cooked tiger prawns, as then you will not have to marinate the mixture in the fridge. This dish works well served with new potatoes or rice and green leaves and the Red onion salad (see page 15).

ingredients

600g salmon fillet, skinned

juice of 4 limes

2 red chillies, seeded and finely chopped

2 tbs coriander, chopped

¼ tsp ground cumin

2 garlic cloves, finely chopped

sea salt and freshly ground black pepper

25g fresh root ginger, peeled and grated

Thai green curry

This is another recipe that always gets rave reviews, there are a lot of ingredients but the paste freezes well, so it is well worth the effort of making a double batch and freezing one half for another day. All the ingredients are available from large supermarkets but I love going to the Thai supermarket to get the lemongrass and lime leaves as theirs are so much bigger, better and cheaper!

Asparagus and sugar snap peas are both a great source of folic acid, which is very important for pregnant women – an essential nutrient for the developing baby's nervous system. Folic acid is also one of the crucial nutrients for breaking down homocysteine in the body – and is therefore important for good cardiovascular health. Homocysteine promotes atherosclerosis by reducing the integrity of blood vessel walls and by interfering with the formation of collagen (the main protein in connective tissue). Elevations in homocysteine are found in approximately 20-40% of patients with heart disease.

DF | **GF** | **WL** use low fat coconut milk

Put all the ingredients for the curry paste in a blender, add some water if necessary to make a barely pourable paste.

Cut the chicken into thin strips and stir-fry with the paste for about 8 minutes. Add the asparagus and then the coconut milk and the bamboo shoots and sugar snap peas. Bring to the boil and cook for a few minutes. Add the lime juice and serve the curry on a bed of lime and coriander rice with a sprinkle of red chilli (for Lime and coriander rice see page 65).

ingredients

for the paste:

2 stalks lemongrass, outer leaves removed and stalks crushed with rolling pin

4 spring onions

3 green chillies, halved and deseeded

4 cloves garlic, roughly chopped

20g fresh root ginger, peeled and roughly chopped

1 bunch coriander

1 tsp coriander seeds

2 tsp cumin seeds, ground

¼ tsp turmeric

6 lime leaves

3 tbs soy sauce

1 tbs fish sauce

juice of 1 lime

for the curry:

2 chicken breasts

1 bunch asparagus, sliced lengthways (I use a runner bean slicer)

400ml coconut milk

225g tin bamboo shoots, drained

100g sugar snap peas

juice of 1 lime

1 red chilli, finely chopped

mains

Japanese style blackened salmon

Another simple recipe that's quick to make and tastes like heaven! My family think this is the absolute best way to eat salmon and I am always cooking it for them.

You can buy mirin and rice vinegar in most good supermarkets and Asian food stores, definitely handy to have in your store cupboard as they are great for making Japanese style salad dressings too.

Mix the mirin, xylitol and soy sauce in a shallow dish and marinate the salmon in it for a few minutes on each side. Heat a large non-stick frying pan on the hob.

Cook the salmon in the pan for a couple of minutes and then turn it over, add the marinade and cook for another few minutes.

Remove salmon to a serving plate, add the rice vinegar to the pan and heat through.

Pour the glaze over the salmon and top with spring onion strips and a sprinkling of sesame seeds.

ingredients

4 tbs mirin

50g xylitol (natural sugar alternative)

4 tbs tamari soy sauce

4 x 125g pieces of salmon

2 tbs rice vinegar

2 spring onions, cut into fine strips

sesame seeds

mains

Sesame salmon

This is another really quick method for cooking salmon in a hurry, I like to serve this with rice or new potatoes to soak up the juice along with some green beans or even frozen peas – a good week night supper ready in a flash.

Ginger contains very potent anti-inflammatory compounds called gingerols. These substances are believed to be why so many people with osteoarthritis or rheumatoid arthritis experience reductions in their pain levels and improvements in their mobility when they consume ginger regularly.

DF **GF** **WL**

Preheat the oven to 180°C/Gas Mark 4.

Place the salmon fillets in an ovenproof dish, cover with the rest of the ingredients. Bake in the centre of the oven for approximately 10 minutes or until the fish is cooked to your liking.

ingredients

4 fillets of salmon, skinless

3 cloves garlic, finely chopped

20g fresh root ginger, grated

3 tsp sesame seeds

3 spring onions, sliced

3 tsp tamari soy sauce

juice of 1 lemon or lime

mains

Salmon fillets with spring onions and green beans

Salmon can be a little uninspiring, which is why I am including several recipes to make you want to eat it more often. This recipe is speedy and delicious – just a matter of combining a few ingredients.

Salmon is rich in the essential omega 3 fatty acids. These fats are lacking in our diet but are crucial to health. A sign that you are lacking in essential fats is if your skin is dry, it should be soft and velvety – so if you are someone to has to smother yourself in body lotion you should consider increasing your intake of nuts and seeds, seed oils and oily fish.

DF | **GF** | **WL** this works well as a meal in itself so skip the potatoes if you are trying to lose weight

Preheat the oven to 180°C/Gas Mark 4.

Blanche the beans in some boiling water for a couple of minutes and drain. Toss the spring onions, cherry tomatoes and blanched green beans in a little olive oil, season with sea salt and freshly ground black pepper, add the basil and place in the bottom of a baking dish. Place the fillets of salmon on top of the vegetables and bake for 10 minutes, or longer if you prefer the fish to be cooked through rather than slightly pink in the middle. Serve with new potatoes.

ingredients

300g green beans

1 bunch spring onions, sliced on the diagonal

150g cherry tomatoes

olive oil

sea salt and freshly ground black pepper

1 handful basil leaves, ripped

4 salmon fillets

mains

Seared tuna steak

Searing tuna steaks literally takes just minutes on a hot griddle and this is exactly the kind of 'fast food' we should be eating. You can marinate it in your own choice of herbs, I like to use a little chilli and lime juice with basil as I always have them to hand, but you might want to try crushed coriander seeds, fresh root ginger – whatever you fancy. Seared tuna goes well with new potatoes and a fresh green salad for a simple supper or lunch.

Tuna is an oily fish and therefore a good source of omega 3 essential fats.

These fats are particularly important for cardiovascular health. Omega 3 fats also reduce the risk of obesity as they improve the body's ability to respond to insulin. A better response to insulin means less insulin is produced and, as this is the storage hormone, that means that less of the food we take in is stored as fat.

Unfortunately because of the high level of mercury in the seas in which it is fished it is not advisable for pregnant women to eat tuna, or for anyone to eat it too often.

DF | GF | WL

Pound the chilli with a little sea salt in a pestle and mortar. Rip up the basil leaves and add to the mix with the lime juice, olive oil and some black pepper. Pour into a shallow dish and coat both sides of the tuna steaks in the marinade.

Heat a griddle or large frying pan. When hot place the tuna steaks on the griddle and sear on each side for a couple of minutes. The longer you leave the fish the less pink it is in the middle.

ingredients

1 red chilli, deseeded and finely sliced

sea salt

1 tbs basil leaves, ripped

juice of 1 lime

2 dsp olive oil

freshly ground black pepper

4 x very fresh tuna steaks, cut thinly

mains

Quick lemon chicken

I was in a rush one day and wanted to cook some chicken asap for the kids. I came up with the brainwave of flattening the chicken first! My friend Al often grills chicken strips on lemongrass skewers for an even better flavour – well worth the effort and great as a BBQ idea.

The leanest part of the chicken is the chicken breast. The fat in chicken is less saturated than red meat fat. However, eating the chicken with the skin doubles the amount of fat and saturated fat in the food. For this reason, chicken is best skinned before cooking.

Use a meat tenderiser to flatten the chicken, or you could bash it a bit and roll it with a rolling pin! Marinate the chicken with the juice and zest from the lemons, the garlic and some olive oil, season with a little salt and black pepper.

Heat a griddle to a high temperature and grill the chicken on both sides so that it is cooked through. Alternatively if you are feeling more adventurous you could thread long strips of the chicken onto soaked wooden skewers (soaking in water for about 20 minutes stops them from burning) or even use lemongrass as skewers and then grill as kebabs.

ingredients

4 skinless chicken breasts

juice and zest of 2 lemons

3 cloves garlic, chopped finely

olive oil

sea salt and freshly ground black pepper

mains

Turkey meatballs with homemade tomato sauce

This recipe works with any mince, I have done it with beef and lamb but prefer turkey as it contains about half the saturated fat of red meat. You can 'hide' any vegetables in the meatballs for picky eaters – I often put in some grated carrot.

Turkey is a very good source of the trace mineral, selenium. Selenium is an essential component for thyroid hormone metabolism, antioxidant defence systems and immune function. Many studies have suggested a strong inverse correlation between selenium intake and cancer incidence.

DF	**GF** use gluten free bread to make the breadcrumbs
WL	steam fry the meatballs with minimum olive oil and a little water

Preheat the oven to 180°C/Gas Mark 4.

Either make the breadcrumbs in a food processor or soak the bread in cold water for a minute, squeeze out the water and crumble the bread into a large bowl. Add all the ingredients and mix well with your hands or a wooden spoon.

Shape the mince mix into balls, about the size of golf balls. Heat a little olive oil in a large heavy-based frying pan and cook the meatballs in batches, until they are golden all over. Transfer to the oven for about 5 minutes to ensure they are cooked through, breaking one apart to make sure there is no pink meat in the middle. Serve with the tomato sauce.

ingredients

breadcrumbs made from 3 slices of wholemeal bread

100g sweetcorn, thawed if frozen

500g turkey mince

1 egg, free range

1 clove garlic, finely chopped

4 spring onions, finely chopped

2 tbs parsley, finely chopped

2 level tbs oregano

1½ tsp sea salt

½ tsp black pepper

olive oil

Tomato sauce

Lycopene is an antioxidant found abundantly in tomatoes and has been shown to be cancer protective. Lycopene is a carotenoid and is fat-soluble, which means it is not well absorbed without fat, so this method of combining tomatoes with olive oil maximises lycopene absorption.

DF	**GF**
WL	steam fry the garlic with minimum oil and a little water

Gently sauté the garlic in the olive oil, add chilli (if using), oregano and tomatoes. Bring to the boil and then simmer for at least half an hour. Add the vinegar and break up the tomatoes with a wooden spoon. Add fresh basil, season with a little sea salt and black pepper, and add a glug of olive oil. Use a hand blender for a smoother sauce. Freeze in portions if you're not using it all at once, this makes a great pasta sauce.

ingredients

2 large cloves garlic, chopped

2 tbs olive oil

1 small chilli – optional, deseeded and chopped finely

1 tsp dried oregano

2 × 400g tins plum tomatoes

½ tbs red wine vinegar

1 handful fresh basil, finely chopped

sea salt and freshly ground black pepper

mains

Healthy fish fingers

This is a recipe that works for any sturdy fish – I tend to use pollock, salmon or cod. It is a great way to get the kids to eat fish – get them to help you make them as they really like getting their hands messy dipping the fish into the different bowls. I make these for Richard too, otherwise he tries to steal them off the kids' plates! These fish fingers freeze well so you could make twice as many and freeze half in plastic containers with greaseproof sheets between to stop them sticking to each other.

Wholemeal bread and flour is always a better choice than the refined white alternatives as wholegrains provide more nutrients as well as important fibre. Refining white flour depletes it of over 90% of its chromium – an important mineral for blood sugar control.

DF	**GF** use brown rice flour for dipping and gluten free bread to make your breadcrumbs	
WL you can bake these in the oven to avoid frying		

I use a food processor to make breadcrumbs, but you could also use a liquidiser, putting in a little bread at a time.

Put the breadcrumbs into a shallow bowl and season with a little sea salt and some black pepper, add the lemon zest.

Put the flour and beaten eggs into two more shallow bowls.

Dip the salmon in the flour to coat it lightly, then dip it into the egg and finally the breadcrumbs.

Heat a little olive oil in a heavy-based frying pan and fry the salmon fingers until golden – a couple of minutes on each side.

Perfect served with new potatoes, a leafy green salad with vine tomatoes and a wedge of lemon or lime. Go easy on the ketchup – it is full of sugar!

ingredients

150g fresh wholemeal breadcrumbs

sea salt and freshly ground black pepper

zest of 1 lemon

60g plain wholemeal flour

2 eggs, beaten

600g salmon fillets, skinless and cut into approximately 8 long strips

olive oil

Salmon fishcakes

This recipe changes slightly every time I make it, sometimes I use sweet potatoes and spring onions, sometimes I use cod or haddock, or a mix of different fish – it depends what mood I'm in, but the basic principle is to use the same amount of fish as potato and then add whatever herbs you fancy. Coriander works well with chilli flakes and kaffir lime leaves if you want more of a Thai taste.

GF use brown rice flour and gluten free breadcrumbs

Peel and chop the potatoes into large chunks and cook in salted boiling water until soft, drain and set aside.

While the potato is cooking poach the salmon in a lidded saucepan in just enough milk to cover. After about four minutes turn off the heat and leave the salmon to cool for about five minutes in the milk. Remove the salmon from the milk and put to one side, reserving some of the milk for making the mashed potato.

Mash the potatoes with a little of the reserved milk and a knob of butter. Add the dill, parsley and capers, the lemon zest and some black pepper. Flake the salmon into the mash.

Put the breadcrumbs, flour and egg into three separate shallow dishes. This is where it gets messy – get a good handful of the fish mixture and form it into a round – dip first in the flour, then the egg and finally the breadcrumbs – and avoid answering the phone as your hands get very gloopy! I usually get about six largish fish cakes out of this recipe.

Fry the fishcakes in olive oil for about four minutes on each side until golden, heating through in the oven if necessary. Serve with wedges of lemon.

ingredients

500g potato

500g salmon fillet, skinless

milk

butter

2 tbs dill, finely chopped

2 tbs parsley, finely chopped

2 tbs capers, rinsed and chopped

zest of 1 lemon

freshly ground black pepper

130g wholemeal breadcrumbs

50g wholemeal flour

2 eggs, beaten

olive oil

Skinny fishcakes

If you are cutting the carbs in the evening then these fishcakes are the answer for a perfect supper, served with a big green salad.

| DF | GF | WL |

Preheat the oven to 200°C/Gas Mark 6.

Marinate the salmon fillet in the lemon juice, garlic and ginger for about half an hour in a baking dish. Bake in the oven for about 10 minutes. Drizzle with a dash of olive oil.

Flake the salmon into a bowl. Add the courgette, pepper, capers and parsley and mix well.

Form the mixture into little rounds with your hands and pat with gluten free flour. Leave for about half an hour in the fridge to set. Steam fry with a little olive oil and water to seal, then bake in the oven for approximately 20 minutes.

ingredients

250g salmon fillet

juice of 1 lemon

2 garlic cloves, chopped finely

30g fresh root ginger, grated

olive oil

1 courgette, grated and squeezed to remove excess water

1 red pepper, very finely sliced

2 tbs capers, chopped

1 tbs parsley, chopped

Doves Farm gluten free flour

Sweet things

Baked peaches with fresh raspberry sauce

This is refreshing and light – the perfect end to a summer's lunch or dinner, even your most health obsessed guests will approve.

You can use strawberries for the sauce or, if you prefer, a mixture of both works really well.

Peaches (and nectarines) are good sources of lycopene and lutein. Lutein gives the red, orange, and yellow colours to fruits and vegetables. These phytochemicals are especially beneficial in the prevention of heart disease, macular degeneration and cancer.

DF avoid the crème fraîche	**GF**	**WL** avoid the crème fraîche or use natural yoghurt

Preheat the oven to 180°C/ Gas Mark 4.

Place the peach halves in a shallow baking dish, cut side up. Drizzle with a little agave nectar.

Sprinkle with the orange zest and pour the orange juice over the peach halves.

Bake the peaches in the oven for about 20 minutes until golden.

Meanwhile put the raspberries in a saucepan with the xylitol and water. Heat through until the xylitol has melted into the raspberries and the mixture is pulpy. Strain the mixture through a sieve reserving the resulting 'sauce' in a jug.

You can enjoy this dish warm or cold. Pour the raspberry sauce over the peaches and serve with a generous blob of crème fraîche.

ingredients

4 peaches, halved and stones removed

agave nectar

juice and zest of 1 orange

1 punnet raspberries

2 tsp xylitol (natural sugar alternative)

1 tbs water

crème fraîche to serve

sweet things

Berry and apple crisp

This is the perfect pud for a Sunday lunch. It is really easy to make and a fun one to get the kids to help you with. You could use whole oats if you are out of muesli and any combination of fruit – pears, raspberries, rhubarb, apricots… they all work well.

Blackberries are one of the fruits lowest in sugars, and are therefore an excellent choice for desserts as well as for smoothies and snacks.

Blackberries are full of antioxidants, they are rich in anthocyanin pigments, responsible for the berries' purplish-black colour – anthocyanins are thought to have anti-inflammatory properties and have been connected with cardiovascular benefits, cancer prevention and cognitive improvement. Blackberries also contain vitamins C and E, and ellagic acid which are also thought to provide protection against cancer and chronic disease. Because of their many tiny seeds, blackberries are a good source of soluble fibre and therefore also play a part in cholesterol lowering.

> **GF** a great muesli is Pertwood Organics wheat free muesli

Preheat the oven to 200°C/Gas Mark 6.

In a heavy-based saucepan cook the apples in a little water with some agave nectar until cooked but still in slices rather than a mush. Melt the butter in a small saucepan and put to the side.

Combine the muesli, almonds, sunflower seeds, flour, cinnamon and xylitol in a bowl.

Tip the blackberries and cooked apple into a shallow baking dish and drizzle with agave nectar.

Stir the melted butter into the crisp topping and spoon on top of the fruit to cover. Bake in the oven for 20 minutes and serve with a dollop of natural yoghurt or crème fraîche.

ingredients

4 medium cooking apples, peeled, cored and sliced

agave nectar

125g unsalted butter or 3 tbs coconut butter

60g unsweetened muesli

40g flaked almonds

30g sunflower seeds

70g brown rice flour (or wholemeal flour if you are not GF)

1 tsp ground cinnamon

75g xylitol (natural sugar alternative)

1 large punnet blackberries

Guilt-free banana chocolate chip loaf

Here is a cake that you can eat without the guilt. Divide the batter into two tins to speed up the cooking time as you will be eager to eat this as soon as possible. Also it means you can eat one and freeze the other for a rainy day.

Xanthan gum is useful in gluten free baking as it prevents the 'sandy' texture which you sometimes get when using gluten free flours. You should be able to find it in your health shop or larger supermarkets.

Bananas are one of our best sources of potassium, an essential mineral for maintaining normal blood pressure and heart function. Since the average banana contains 467mg of potassium and only 1mg of sodium, a banana a day may help to prevent high blood pressure and protect against atherosclerosis.

DF	GF	WL

Preheat the oven to 180°C/Gas Mark 4.

Lightly grease two loaf tins (or use half the quantities and just make one small cake).

In a medium bowl mix the flour, baking powder, xanthan gum, salt and cinnamon. Heat the coconut butter in a saucepan and allow to cool a little. Add to the mixture along with the agave nectar, soya milk and vanilla extract. Stir well and then gently fold in the banana and chocolate chips. Divide the mixture evenly between the two tins and bake in the oven for 20-30 minutes, until a skewer pushed into the centre of the loaf comes out clean. Leave to cool for 20 minutes before tipping out of the tins, most delicious served warm!

ingredients

280g Doves Farm gluten free brown bread flour

2 tsp baking powder

1 tsp xanthan gum

1 tsp sea salt

1 tsp ground cinnamon

110g coconut butter

230g agave nectar

140ml soya milk

1 tsp vanilla extract

4 ripe mashed bananas

70g dark chocolate chips

Pistachio cake

This is a lovely cake, it is not too sweet and perfect as a dessert with yoghurt and berries or cold as a tea time treat.

Pistachios are a great source of copper, manganese and phosphorus, which all play a part in building strong, healthy bones. They also contain significant amounts of potassium and magnesium, which help regulate heart rate and blood pressure.

GF

WL this is a good cake if you are watching your weight as it is sugar free and contains relatively little fat. Remember that coconut butter is more likely to be used as energy and therefore is less likely to be stored on your hips!

Heat the oven to 180°C/Gas Mark 4.

Grease a 23cm springform tin and dust with flour. Put the eggs in a bowl with the xylitol and beat until pale and thick. Mix in the yoghurt and oil/coconut oil, then fold in the ground pistachios, flour and baking powder.

Pour the mixture into the tin and bake for approximately 40 minutes, until a skewer comes out clean. Allow the cake to cool in the tin for 15 minutes, then turn out onto a wire rack to cool completely. If you like, use a small sieve to dust with icing sugar.

For a delicious dessert, serve with Greek yoghurt and fresh berries.

ingredients

4 eggs

100g xylitol (natural sugar alternative)

150g natural yoghurt

70ml olive oil or melted organic extra virgin coconut butter

100g shelled unsalted pistachios, ground finely in a food processor

100g brown rice flour or Doves Farm brown bread gluten free flour

1 tsp baking powder

1 heaped tsp icing sugar

Orange almond torte

This recipe is adapted from one in Natalie Savona's fantastic book *Wonderfoods*. It works every time, is a real doddle to make and great if you are on a gluten free diet.

This is delicious served warm as a dessert with thick natural yoghurt and raspberries.

Almonds are good for cardiovascular health, this is due partly to the antioxidant action of the vitamin E found in these nuts, as well as to the cholesterol-lowering effect of their monounsaturated fats.

Put the whole, unpeeled oranges in a pan and add cold water to cover. Bring to the boil, cover and simmer for 1 hour. Drain the oranges and leave them to cool.

Preheat the oven to 180°C/Gas Mark 4.

Grease a 23cm springform round cake tin. Cut the oranges into chunks and remove the pips, then tip them into a food processor. Add the remaining ingredients and process until evenly blended, then pour the mixture into the cake tin. Bake for 45-60 minutes until risen and firm. Turn the torte out on to a wire rack to cool completely. Dust with a little icing sugar.

ingredients

2 large oranges

170g xylitol (natural sugar alternative)

200g ground almonds

4 eggs

juice of ½ lemon

1 tsp baking powder

1 heaped tsp icing sugar

sweet things

Lemon berry muffins

These muffins are always a big hit at my workshops, they appeal to everyone as they are both gluten free and definitely guilt free!

Berries are easily available year round as you can buy them frozen from most supermarkets. I always keep a supply in the freezer for smoothies and muffins. Berries are rich in manganese and vitamin C, so are good for joints and excellent for supporting the immune system.

DF use soya milk and coconut butter | **GF**

WL definitely acceptable as a treat as these muffins contain very little fat and no sugar

Preheat the oven to 200°C/Gas Mark 6.

Melt the butter in a small saucepan and leave to cool. Stir together the corn flour, almonds, baking powder, xylitol and lemon zest. In a measuring jug pour in the lemon juice and enough milk to reach the 200ml mark, then beat in the egg and melted butter. Pour into the dry ingredients and stir together briefly. Fold in the berries and spoon the mixture into a greased 12-bun muffin tray. Bake for approximately 25 minutes, leave to cool in the tray for five minutes and then turn out onto a rack and cool thoroughly.

ingredients

60g butter

100g yellow corn flour
(from health food shop)

100g ground almonds

2 rounded tsp baking powder

150g xylitol (natural sugar alternative)

juice and zest of 1 unwaxed lemon

120ml milk

1 large egg

150g fresh or frozen berries

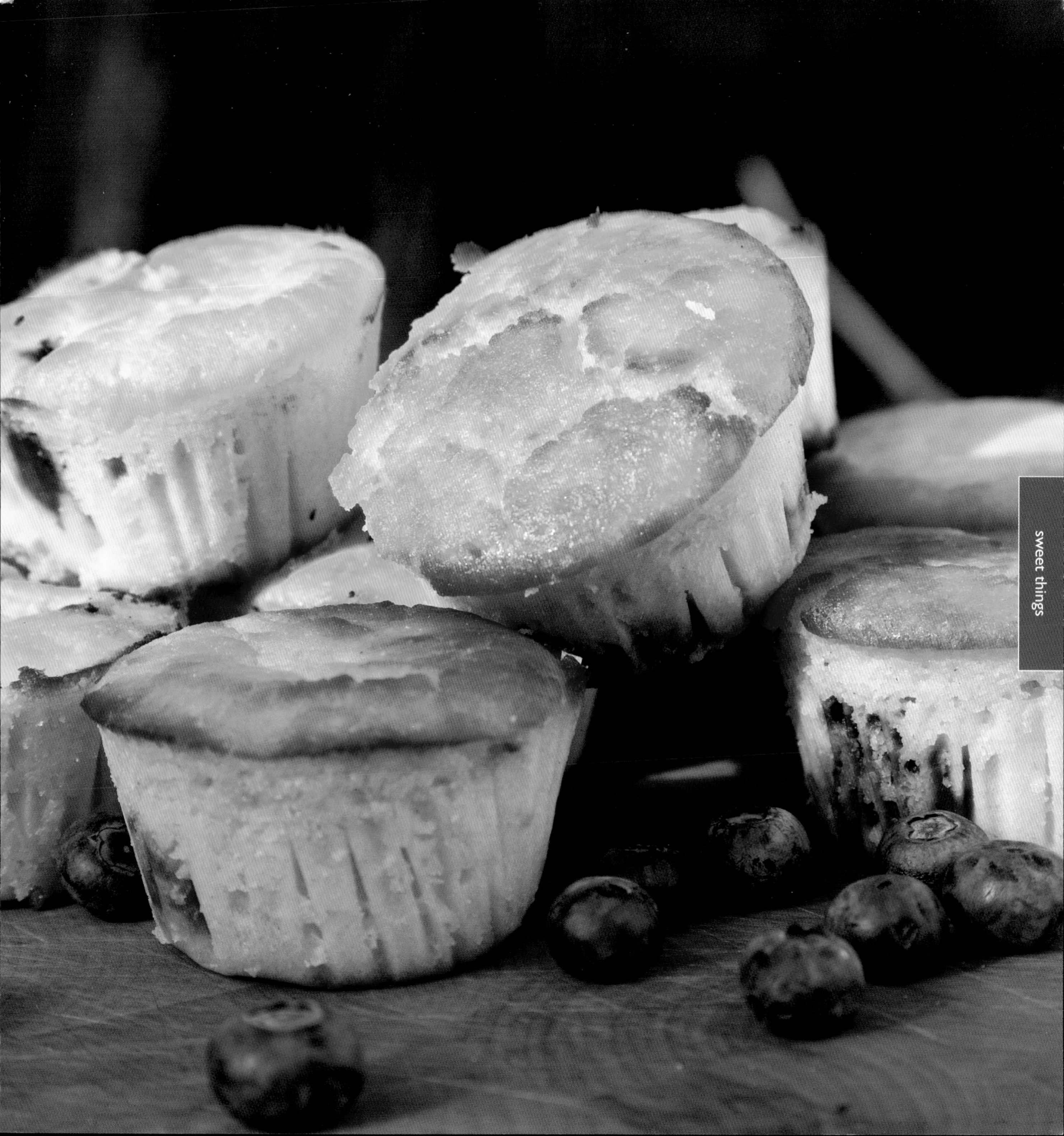

Butternut squash cake

Here is a good way to get more vegetable goodness into the children!
You could use this recipe to make muffins, just remember that they will only
need 20 minutes to cook.

Butternut squash is a great source of beta-carotene, which has been shown
to have very powerful antioxidant and anti-inflammatory properties.
Beta-carotene is able to prevent the oxidation of cholesterol in the body.
As oxidised cholesterol is the type that builds up in blood vessel walls and
contributes to the risk of heart attack and stroke, getting plenty of beta-
carotene in the diet may help to prevent the progression of atherosclerosis.

DF **GF** **WL**

Preheat the oven to 180°C/Gas Mark 4.

Cut the squash in half and remove the seeds. Place on a baking tray cut side up and
roast until soft, approximately 30 minutes. Remove from the oven and allow to cool
before puréeing the flesh in a food processor. Butter and flour a loaf tin or a 23cm
springform tin.

In a bowl sift together the flour, baking powder, xanthan gum, nutmeg, mace and
cinnamon, and set aside. In another bowl whisk together the eggs and xylitol. Add the
squash purée, orange zest and oil and stir. Add the chopped dates, walnuts and flour
and fold into the mixture. Spoon the mixture into the prepared tin. Bake in the lower
third of the oven for about 55 minutes, until a skewer comes out clean. Allow to cool
for 10 minutes before turning out onto a rack.

ingredients

1 small butternut squash (approx 700g)

170g brown rice flour

1 tsp baking powder

1 tsp xanthan gum

½ tsp grated nutmeg

¼ tsp ground mace

½ tsp ground cinnamon

2 large eggs

150g xylitol (natural sugar alternative)

zest of 1 orange

4 tbs olive oil

125g pitted dates, sliced

1 handful walnuts

sweet things

Carrot muffins

I have been making a version of these muffins for 20 years – I used to make a cake in a 7-inch tin using the same basic recipe, and even posted one to Paris once to impress a new boyfriend! For a treat I sometimes blob on some cream cheese icing: made simply by combining a pot of cream cheese with a little lemon juice and enough icing sugar to get just the right sweetness.

Carrots are an excellent source of antioxidant compounds, and the richest vegetable source of the pro-vitamin A carotenes. Carrots' antioxidant compounds help protect against cardiovascular disease and cancer and also promote good vision, especially night vision.

DF **GF** **WL** use xylitol in place of soft brown sugar

Preheat the oven to 180°C/Gas Mark 4.

Line the muffin tin with 12 paper cases. Whisk the eggs with the brown sugar and gradually add the olive oil or melted coconut butter. Add the rest of the ingredients, any dried fruit works so add whatever you fancy, you may like to add seeds too – cardamon seeds work well, as do sunflower seeds. Pour the mixture into the muffin cases.

Cook in the centre of the oven for approximately 15 minutes until a skewer comes out clean. Remove from the oven and cool on a wire rack.

ingredients

2 eggs

90g soft brown sugar

100ml olive oil or coconut butter

180g carrot, grated

120g brown rice flour

1 tsp baking powder

1 tsp ground cinnamon

½ tsp of ground nutmeg

1 handful sultanas or raisins

1 handful chopped dried apricots

1 handful walnuts

60g desiccated coconut

sweet things

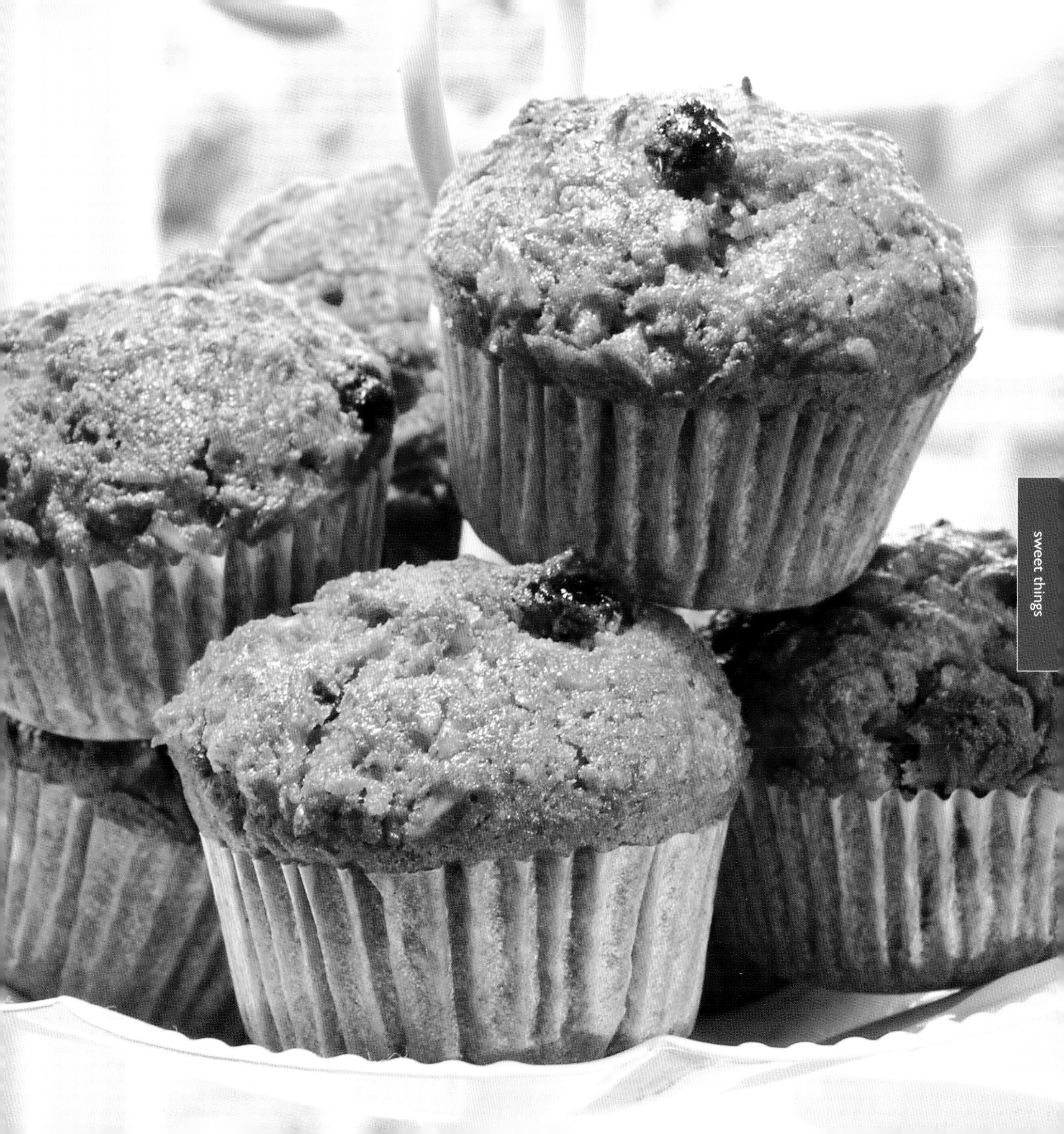

Chocolate chip cookies

These cookies are delicious and full of healthy ingredients. I tend to put chocolate chips in when I am making them with my children but they are also delicious with sultanas in place of the chips.

It is thought that a class of compounds found in citrus fruit peels called polymethoxylated flavones (PMFs) have the potential to lower cholesterol more effectively than some prescription drugs. Grating a tablespoon or so of the peel from a well-scrubbed organic orange each day and using it to flavour tea, salads, salad dressings, soups, or in this case cookies, may be a practical way of achieving some cholesterol-lowering benefits.

DF **GF**

Preheat the oven to 180°C/Gas Mark 4.

Grease a couple of large baking trays.

Cream the butter and xylitol together and then gradually beat in the banana, vanilla extract and egg. Add the orange zest and combine the ingredients until well blended.

In a large bowl mix the flour, salt, baking powder, oats, coconut and chocolate chips. Add the butter mixture and combine all of the ingredients so that they are thoroughly mixed. Form rounds with the dough (using about a tablespoon of the mixture for each cookie), place each round on the baking sheet and press to flatten – leave a couple of centimetres between each. Bake for approximately 15 minutes until golden and cool on a wire rack.

ingredients

115g unsalted butter at room temperature, or melted organic extra virgin coconut butter

100g xylitol (natural sugar alternative)

40g mashed banana

1 tsp vanilla extract

1 egg

grated zest of 1 orange

125g Doves Farm gluten free brown bread flour

¼ tsp salt

1 tsp gluten free baking powder

120g rolled oats

20g desiccated coconut

75g dark chocolate chips

sweet things

Granola bars

This recipe is based on the granola bars given to clients on New You Boot Camps – it is given out as a mid-morning snack and the Boot Campers love it!

Oats contain a specific type of fibre known as beta-glucan. Studies show that in individuals with high cholesterol, consuming oat fibre daily significantly decreases cholesterol. Lowering high cholesterol levels can reduce the risk of cardiovascular disease and stroke.

Studies also show that beta-glucan has beneficial effects in diabetes. Type 2 diabetes patients given foods high in this type of oat fibre experience much lower rises in blood sugar compared to those given white rice or bread. Starting out your day with a blood sugar stabilising food such as oats may make it easier to keep blood sugar levels under control for the rest of the day.

DF | **WL**

Preheat the oven to 180°C/Gas Mark 4.

Place the dried fruit in a pan with the water and heat until the fruit is softened – for about 5 minutes.

Add the agave nectar and treacle to the fruit. Add the seeds.

Add the oats and remaining ingredients and then press the mixture into a lined Swiss roll tin (18cm x 28cm). Bake in the oven for approximately 20 minutes.

ingredients

250g mixed dried fruit
(this can be whatever you fancy: peaches, apricots, cranberries, pears, etc.)

150ml water

1 tbsp agave nectar

½ tbsp black treacle

80g mixed seeds

250g porridge oats

50g desiccated coconut

75ml olive oil

1 tsp ground cinnamon

1 tsp mixed spice

sweet things

Charles's healthy fruit cake

Charles is a chef I met on one of my in:spa retreats, he made this amazing fruit cake and the clients couldn't believe their luck as they were expecting to suffer on a detox diet all week!

The benefits of black tea are often written about in health features as tea is known to be a good source of antioxidants. The problem is that as a nation we tend to drink way too much of it and as tea contains caffeine it can have a negative impact on our health – caffeine in excess upsets blood sugar balance and can reduce absorption of certain minerals from the food we eat. I advise my clients to stop at two cups a day.

DF | **GF** | **WL**

Preheat the oven to 170°C/Gas Mark 3.

Line a 22cm cake tin.

Cream together the butter/coconut butter with the xylitol. Add the eggs and the flour with the baking powder. Add the drained dried fruit along with the ground almonds and orange and lemon zest. Add the nuts and fold everything together until fully mixed, transfer to the lined cake tin.

Bake for approximately 1½ hours until a skewer comes out clean. Cool on a wire rack.

ingredients

150g butter or organic extra virgin coconut butter

150g xylitol (natural sugar alternative)

3 eggs, beaten

225g Doves Farm gluten free brown bread flour

1 tsp baking powder

450g mixed dried fruit, soaked in tea and drained

2 tbs ground almonds

zest of 1 orange

zest of 1 lemon

50g whole nuts

sweet things

What people say about Alli

"Thank you for the wonderful cookery workshop last night. What a fabulous evening! Very much looking forward to cooking up the meals."

Gill - workshop participant

"Thank you for such a wonderful, healthy and inspiring cooking session last Thursday. The format is perfect – relaxed and open and friendly and a real change from stuffy cooking! I've already made a quinoa salad to great success and can't wait to make the chicken soup..." **Leila** - workshop participant

"My health, my family, my budget and my kitchen confidence have all been boosted by my time with Alli. Her approach to cooking is down-to-earth and realistic for the stresses of our daily lives. The anxiety of what to make for dinner is instantly quelled when I reach for my collection of Alli recipes. I know that I can pull one out and make a fresh, amazing, lovely and appreciated meal for myself and my family without the stress of my pre-Alli existence." **Beth** – workshop participant

"Before I went to see Alli for some help and advice I was stuck in a rut with my weight and had got to the point where I felt like I'd tried every diet going and was very fed up. Alli was so positive right from the start, and put me at my ease. She went at my pace, fine tuning a diet to suit me and my needs. I found the diet itself hard going to begin with as I'd had so many years of over eating and eating the wrong things. Alli made sure that I checked in with her regularly and gave me constant support. I would often phone or text her in the first couple of weeks in a panic and she would be fantastic at calming me down and getting me back on track again. I have seen fantastic results from this diet, and with Alli's help I lost a large amount of weight. After 12 weeks I am now on the right path, so I am able to confidently follow my own healthy eating plan without going off the rails." **Katie** – client and workshop participant

"Alli has taught me a lot of good healthy recipes at the workshops. As well as being fun, easy and packed with nutrition, I come home feeling that I've eaten fabulous food. Also the focus is not on what you can't eat, but what you can and the little changes you can do to make your normal everyday foods healthier. Through the workshops I have learnt not just how to make new dishes, but I've taken recipes I've used for ages and changed them according to what Alli's taught me." **Linn** – workshop participant

About Alli

A nutritionist regularly interviewed on TV and radio and quoted in the press, Alli began her career as a fashion model. Travelling the world gave her an opportunity to sample many local cuisines – including those of Japan, Italy and France – and presented her with a mission to combine exciting culinary experiences with optimum health.

Back in the UK, Alli qualified as a nutritionist, initially setting up a practice within a chain of health clubs, as well as working alongside local GPs and for The Food Doctor. Alli currently provides services as a nutritional therapist for in:spa retreats and New You Boot Camps, as well as managing her own practice, offering private consultations

and cookery workshops from her home in London. She also enjoys working in the community, teaching healthy eating and cooking at the Asian Centre in North London, and to people with disabilities and special needs through the Adventures in Eating project.

index

index